MEASURES OF SUCCESS

React Less, Lead Better, Improve More

Also by Mark Graban

LEAN HOSPITALS

Improving Quality, Patient Safety, and Employee Engagement

(3RD EDITION, 2016) — AVAILABLE IN EIGHT LANGUAGES — SHINGO RESEARCH AWARD

HEALTHCARE KAIZEN

Engaging Front-Line Staff in Sustainable Continuous Improvements

(CO-AUTHORED BY JOE SWARTZ) — SHINGO RESEARCH AWARD

THE EXECUTIVE GUIDE TO HEALTHCARE KAIZEN

Leadership for a Continuously Learning and Improving Organization

(CO-AUTHORED BY JOE SWARTZ)

PRACTICING LEAN

Learning How to Learn How to get Better… Better

(ANTHOLOGY EDITED BY MARK GRABAN, WITH 15 OTHER AUTHORS)

Quick Endorsements

"With clarity and precision, Mark Graban steps through the process of collecting and analyzing the kind of data you focus on... If you're navigating a tough business environment, you need this book."

DANIEL H. PINK | AUTHOR OF *WHEN* AND *DRIVE*

"Mark Graban has written a readable, informative book to guide any leader who wants to help an organization achieve true and lasting success. Improvement has been made easier thanks to his work."

ERIC RIES | AUTHOR OF *THE LEAN STARTUP* AND *THE STARTUP WAY*

"The data-driven decision-making techniques in this book will stop you from confusing activity with progress and—finally—get things done."

QUINT STUDER | FOUNDER, STUDER COMMUNITY INSTITUTE | AUTHOR OF BOOKS, INCLUDING *HARDWIRING EXCELLENCE*

"Mark has hit another home run... the book that everyone who is serious about improvement needs to read."

DAN MARKOVITZ | FOUNDER OF MARKOVITZ CONSULTING | AUTHOR OF *A FACTORY OF ONE* AND *BUILDING THE FIT ORGANIZATION*

"This book brings much-needed clarity to this important topic and will be invaluable to anyone seeking to make sustainable improvements to their processes."

HARVEY LEACH | PRINCIPAL CONSULTANT, THE CONSULTANCY COMPANY, OXFORD, ENGLAND

"This book outlines in understandable terms the complex world of performance measurement."

DR. JOHN TOUSSAINT | EXECUTIVE CHAIRMAN AND CEO, CATALYSIS | AUTHOR OF BOOKS, INCLUDING *ON THE MEND*

"... an engaging and practical guide... an essential addition to any Lean or Six Sigma learning library."

JON MILLER | PARTNER, GEMBA ACADEMY | AUTHOR OF *CREATING A KAIZEN CULTURE*

"Mark Graban taught the KaiNexus team how to understand the story a metric is actually telling over time. We've saved time by not overanalyzing every up and down in our metrics — and that's valuable time we now put to better use."

DR. GREG JACOBSON | CEO AND CO-FOUNDER, KAINEXUS

"Mark has produced an excellent book to help improvement professionals and leaders alike gain clarity about how their processes are actually performing to drive more relevant improvement. Bravo!"

KAREN MARTIN | PRESIDENT, TKMG, INC. | AUTHOR OF BOOKS, INCLUDING *CLARITY FIRST* AND *THE OUTSTANDING ORGANIZATION*

"[Mark] shows us precisely how to avoid the data-interpretation traps that can lead us astray in our attempts to improve our systems."

MATTHEW E. MAY | AUTHOR, *THE ELEGANT SOLUTION* AND *WINNING THE BRAIN GAME*

"I've long thought the world would be a better place if everyone took a statistics class, but this book is much better (and shorter)!"

CRAIG DEAO | MANAGING DIRECTOR, SPEAKER, AUTHOR — STUDER GROUP, A HURON SOLUTION

"Too often, organizations waste time and energy responding to short-term fluctuations in performance that do not reflect sustained trends. *Measures of Success* provides leaders with a blueprint for separating signal from noise and focusing resources on lasting improvement."

ZEYNEP TON | ADJUNCT ASSOCIATE PROFESSOR AT MIT SLOAN SCHOOL OF MANAGEMENT | AUTHOR OF *THE GOOD JOBS STRATEGY*

Table of Contents

Foreword

I t is an honor to have the privilege to write a foreword for this book by my friend Mark Graban. He has created a guide for using and understanding the data that surround us every day. These numbers are constantly changing. They go up, and they go down. But what do these changes signify? Some of the changes in the data will represent real changes in the underlying system or process that generated the data. Other changes will simply represent the routine variation in the underlying system when nothing has changed.

So the problem with interpreting the data is deciding when a change in the data represents a real change in the system and when it does not. As a result, there are two ways we can get things right and two ways we can get things wrong. We get things right when the system changes and we interpret the change in the data as a signal of that change. We also get things right when the system does not change and we interpret the change in the data as being merely noise.

We get things wrong when the system does not change but we interpret the data as representing a change. This is the error of interpreting noise as a signal. We also get things wrong when the system changes and we interpret the data as representing no change. This is the error of missing a signal.

Since everyone understands the problem of missing a signal, we usually seek to avoid this error by interpreting every change as a signal. The numbers go up, and that's a signal. The numbers go down, and that's a signal. The numbers stay the same, and that's a signal, too (because we expected them to go up or down). As we run around crying that "the sky is falling," we do occasionally get it right, but more often than not, we are simply interpreting noise as a signal.

Mark presents the antidote to this disease of interpreting noise as signals. And that is why everyone who is exposed to business data of any type needs to read this book.

Donald J. Wheeler, Ph.D.

KNOXVILLE | 8 JUNE 2018

Preface

Why did I write this book? I want you and your organization to be more successful, to improve more, and to be less frustrated in your improvement efforts. My intent is that this book's methods will help managers, executives, business owners, and improvement specialists in any industry use limited time more effectively.

As I've worked and talked with leaders throughout my career, I've heard many common challenges that aren't always easily articulated. One leader expressed a vague underlying concern:

> "We're trying really hard, but this approach [of managing]... I don't know; it seems not to be working."

For all of the attention placed on performance, goals, and metrics, many leaders haven't been taught the most modern and effective ways to improve and gauge progress. Some of our common management practices, as taught in business schools or passed down from generation to generation, can actually interfere with improvement. There is a better way.

I see many well-intended leaders doing what they think is best for the organization and their customers. Or, they're doing what they think is necessary. But, some of their best efforts and long hours often end up being a waste of time. Leaders and their employees get stressed out; they react; but are they more effective as a result?

Accepting a better way requires first that we recognize problems or shortcomings with current management practices.

Another leader told me:

> "We have an old-school, command-and-control (if not bullying) culture. Leaders demand better performance and throw goals at people, whether they're achievable or not. They celebrate when we make a small improvement and come down on us when performance dips.

They throw solutions at us instead of helping us develop our improvements. We're trying to shift from a blame-and-shame culture to a data-driven culture."

I've seen too much workplace bullying throughout my career. I've seen far too many leaders blaming employees for a system's poor performance. It's especially sad to see in healthcare, where the human stakes are so high for everyone involved.

The best efforts of individuals might not be enough to guarantee success for a team or the organization as a whole. We often see great people being defeated by their broken workplace. For example, think of the famous scene from the *I Love Lucy* show with Lucy and Ethel in the chocolate factory. They're working hard, and they can't keep up. A badly designed or managed system defeats good people every time, as they say.

Far too often, leaders at all levels are in the same predicament as Lucy and Ethel. They're under enormous pressure to improve. They aren't meeting their targets. Bad results and problems are flying at them faster than they can handle, like chocolates on a conveyor belt. So, everybody is working hard to improve — but the management methods we've been taught might not be enough to make a difference.

Thankfully, many organizations are very intentionally trying to move toward more collaborative and participatory management styles. I think this book will help people work together better in the name of improvement.

A different leader said:

> "We're not very good at using data to inform daily decisions and problem solving. We're trying to build that culture. We need to push daily metrics."

As we'll discuss in this book, daily metrics can be more helpful than weekly or monthly metrics. In so many settings, I've seen leaders draw poor conclusions about single data points (or two data points). More data points might just mean more overreaction. Again, there is a better way.

I'm fortunate to have learned and used some methods that enable better management decision making. I'm happy I can share them with others. These methods, grounded in math and science, help us to be more data driven and to make better decisions that are based on facts instead of opinions, hunches, or feelings. Doing so will reduce the amount of time we spend chasing our tail, if you will, in the name of improvement. We can turn data, metrics, and charts into knowledge, wisdom, action, and better results.

I wouldn't call this a "statistics book." I'd consider it to be a "management book" that happens to draw upon a few simple statistical concepts and methods. These methods aren't complicated; they're just different. Anyone can use them without a Six Sigma "Belt" or a statistics degree.

Using these methods, we can learn how to distinguish between activity that adds value to the customer and activity that's wasted motion. Not all motion or effort is useful, even for leaders. We might take pride in being busy, but, a lot of management activity doesn't lead to progress.

One leader told me:

> "Our team meets daily and talks about our metrics. They get better, and then they get worse. Our monthly strategic reviews are the same thing but on a monthly basis. Instead of stating the obvious, such as 'that measure is better than before,' can we move to a deeper understanding of our data that leads to real improvement?"

This book will show you how to draw more timely, more valid conclusions based on your metrics, leading to more focused and effective improvement.

These methods come from a line of legendary thinkers, including the famed management guru W. Edwards Deming, known as "the American who taught the Japanese about quality" after World War II. Deming learned from Walter Shewhart, who invented the "Statistical Process Control" (SPC) methods that Deming built upon to create a broader system of management that included a knowledge of variation, appreciation for a system, psychology, and the theory of knowledge.[1]

More recently, Donald J. Wheeler, Ph.D. has built upon and spread these methods, including what he dubbed "Process Behavior Charts."[2] He has inspired many, including me, through his seminal book *Understanding Variation*. I was very fortunate that my father, Bob, had a copy of Dr. Wheeler's book (along with Deming's *Out of the Crisis*) after being a student in classes they taught at General Motors. My browsing of his bookshelf piqued my interest in these topics and opened my eyes to a different way — one that I've learned to be a better way. And, I'm extremely honored that Dr. Wheeler wrote the foreword for this book.

Working in many industries has allowed me to test and validate the practical nature of these methods, even if they were not in sync with the organizational culture as a whole. I'm convinced these methods can be impactful, which is why I feel driven to share them through this book and my consulting work.

As Dr. Wheeler says, these management and statistical methods are "a way of thinking, with some tools attached."[3]

By reading this book, you'll learn new methodologies and this new way of thinking. Once you learn to understand variation, it's impossible to unlearn. You'll see opportunities to apply these principles every day — in everyday life and your workplace. Hopefully, we can agree that metrics and targets should be used for improvement, not for punishment. I hope this book is helpful. Thanks for reading.

Mark Graban

25 JUNE 2018

Acknowledgments and Dedications

Many thanks to my editor, Cheryl Fenske, and my book coach, Cathy Fyock. I'd like to also thank early readers who gave valuable feedback and helped make this a better book. They include Mike Stoecklein, Shrikant Kalegaonkar, Warren Stokes, Dan Markovitz, Dan Ackerman, Harvey Leach, and Lewis Lefteroff.

My greatest thanks are due to my loving wife and partner, Amy Gowder Graban. I also thank my parents, Bob and Marlene Graban, and my in-laws, Charlie and Debbie Gowder. All of them have encouraged my learning and writing over the years. Finally, I'd like to thank the countless number of people who have taken time to teach and mentor me over the years.

Introduction

This book presents a practical, simple method ("Process Behavior Charts") that separates "signal" from "noise" in our metrics (a.k.a. "performance measures"), so we can learn when and how to evaluate and respond to our metrics appropriately over time. By using this method and overreacting less often (or reacting in different ways), we can stop wasting time and start improving more. This will also reduce frustration in the workplace and boost performance through higher morale and increased engagement.

I hope this book will be helpful to many types of readers, including those who will *create* Process Behavior Charts (including analysts, process improvement specialists, quality department staff, et al.) and those who will primarily *consume* and use such charts and metrics (including managers, executives, business owners, venture capitalists, and others).

CHAPTER 1 introduces the idea of "what gets measured gets managed" but takes a deeper dive into what "managed" means. Topics in the chapter include choosing the right metrics, the danger of arbitrary targets, and the case for why Process Behavior Charts matter: leaders and employees can waste less time "chasing the noise" in a metric, which allows them to spend more time on systematic and sustainable improvement.

CHAPTERS 2 AND 3 introduce the Process Behavior Chart method and how to use such charts. Comparisons are drawn to some common existing methods for tracking metrics and evaluating performance against targets. Why are Process Behavior Charts more effective than two-data-point comparisons, "Bowling Charts," and the like?

CHAPTER 4 connects charts and metrics to our goals of improvement and success. The chapter explores methods for turning an unpredictable system into a predictable system by reacting to signals and, then, how to improve a predictable system in less-reactive ways.

CHAPTER 5 is a narrative description of an exercise that's effective in learning how to understand variation: "The Red Bead Game" that was made famous by the late, great Dr. W. Edwards Deming. Readers will have a chance to reflect on some of the common management tactics that are generally ineffective in a real workplace.

CHAPTER 6 shows how Process Behavior Charts can be used to dig deeper, beyond statistics found in news headlines. How are comparisons between two data points sometimes misleading? Does the "highest number in X years" mean that there's a significant shift in our data?

CHAPTER 7 further compares Process Behavior Charts to common management methods and analysis approaches, including linear trend lines, column charts, and more.

CHAPTER 8 comes back to workplace case studies and how we would use Process Behavior Charts to make better management decisions.

CHAPTER 9 explores ideas related to change management and successfully introducing a new method into an organization.

APPENDIX A takes a deeper dive, for those who need it, into the process and method for creating Process Behavior Charts.

The book also includes 10 "Key Points" that will be introduced and revisited, along with three "Core Questions" that we should ask about systems and metrics.

Summary of Key Points
from *Measures of Success*

KEY POINT #1: We don't manage the metric; we manage the system that leads to the results, and we lead the people who help us improve the system.

KEY POINT #2: Two data points are not a trend.

KEY POINT #3: "No data have meaning apart from their context."

KEY POINT #4: A chart will always tell us more than a list of numbers.

KEY POINT #5: The job of management is not just to look backward, but also to look forward and predict, if possible, what is likely to occur.

KEY POINT #6: There is variation in every metric or data set. Process Behavior Charts filter out noise so we can identify signals.

KEY POINT #7: Don't waste time explaining noise in a metric. There is no simple, single "root cause" for noise.

KEY POINT #8: More timely data are better for improvement. Daily is better than weekly, which is better than monthly, as long as we don't overreact to every data point.

KEY POINT #9: If there was an intervention in the system, make it clear in your chart or your discussion of the chart when that change was started or implemented.

KEY POINT #10: When showing the "before" scenario, show enough data points to illustrate the previous level of variation, not just a single data point.

CHAPTER 1

Improving the Way
We Improve

Most organizations are under pressure to perform better. How do we increase sales and production in our family-owned manufacturing company? Can we reduce infection rates in a hospital's intensive care unit? Will we get our startup on the growth trajectory that we promised the venture capital firm?

People often feel like they're on a proverbial performance roller coaster. There are a lot of ups and downs. There's anticipation, excitement, and sometimes yelling — whether from excitement or fear. The emotional roller coaster of metrics and the way leaders react (or overreact) to them can be exhausting. This book is meant to help you get off the performance roller coaster, both stabilizing and systematically improving your results instead of ending up right back where you started.

Leaders might be under pressure to judge performance on a daily (or even hourly) basis. Color coding performance as "red is bad, green is good" can lead to a lot of overreaction, which then wastes the time of managers and their employees. Does any of this help us improve?

In an age of "big data," we are too often drowning in numbers and information. Using the methods in this book, we can turn a flood of data into a controlled flow of knowledge and insight that allows us to evaluate performance better, focusing our efforts on sustainable improvement instead of knee-jerk reactions. When do our reactions, no matter how well intended, end up hampering improvement?

The desire (or need) to improve doesn't mean that an organization knows how to do so. It doesn't mean leaders know how to look at their performance measures in ways that determine if they are actually improving. Do they *know* how to look for meaningful changes in performance, or are they guessing or relying on gut feel? Do they use rules of thumb, such as "you must investigate and explain every data point that's below the target" or "you must find a root cause and give a corrective action plan for every below-average week?"

> In an age of "big data," we might be drowning
> in numbers and information.

Leaders might ask the following questions:

- Are we reaching our goals or targets?
- What do we expect our future performance to be?
- How do we know if a change has led to a meaningful improvement?
- Can we discover if a system's performance is degrading before it falls back into the red?
 How often are leaders pressured to *make metrics look good* instead of improving the system and its underlying performance?

Some leaders might not ask those questions. Or, they might not know how to answer all of them. This book will help us answer the first four questions. The fifth is something to think about and consider for your own setting.

Measures Matter, but Don't Forget About Managing

An expression that's often shared on social media or in email signatures is:

> "What gets measured, gets managed."

A statement like this emphasizes the importance of measurement, but it's frustratingly vague about how to manage or improve what is measured. Focusing on "what gets measured" is the reality in modern organizations. Measuring is easy; managing is hard.

Organizations often measure too many things, losing sight that the "K" in the common "KPI" acronym means "*Key* Performance Indicators," not "*Ka-jillion*

Performance Indicators." More measures might mean more work — and possibly more overreaction — instead of more improvement.

When under pressure to improve metrics, leaders and employees will pay attention. They'll talk about the metrics. They might assign somebody to be responsible for each one. They might form teams. That doesn't mean they know the best way to manage the metric, and it doesn't mean they know how to improve the system that generates those results.

> Measuring is easy; managing is hard.

Can we measure everything in life (or our workplace) that matters? No, as Deming said:

> "The most important figures that one needs for management are unknown or unknowable, but successful management must nevertheless take account of them."4

The reality is that we have to do our best to choose measures that matter (or our boss tells us what to measure) — and then manage those measures in the best (or least dysfunctional) way possible.

What Are the Right Metrics?

Leaders are often told what to measure, causing organizational harm and dysfunction. Sometimes, we get the opportunity to choose metrics or have some input. Hopefully, we have metrics that matter instead of things that are easy to measure.

While there is a risk that the methods in this book could be used to "better manage" the wrong metrics, the focus of this book is to best manage and improve the metrics that we have. For a deeper treatment about what metrics to choose and how to set targets, books on the following methodologies could be helpful (see Appendix C):

- Balanced Scorecard
- Strategy Deployment
- Lean Startup

A "balanced scorecard" of metrics helps protect against the dysfunctions that can result from focusing too much on any single metric. For example, if cost is the primary metric, managers might be pressured into actions that hurt safety, quality, or other important measures. Think of all of the problems caused by companies that focused solely on growth at any cost.

Strategy deployment (or "hoshin kanri," in Japanese) is an important component of the "Lean" management approach.[5] Lean organizations in various industries often use a balanced scorecard of metrics such as safety, quality, delivery, cost, and morale. These metrics should be relatable to people at all levels, so they feel like they can initiate improvements that contribute to their local metrics and the success of the organization as a whole.

From "Vanity Metrics" to "Actionable Metrics"

The "Lean Startup" movement asks important questions about what to measure. Eric Ries coined the phrase "vanity metrics" to describe our measures that "give the rosiest possible picture."[6] Instead of looking at the things that paint a picture of success, we should look at metrics that are truly our KPIs for our organization.

If we're using metrics to evaluate the success of an improvement initiative, are we choosing metrics or manipulating them to tell a story of success, no matter what actually happened? Or, are we using metrics honestly to evaluate if we are getting better, getting worse, or if we're in the awkward in-between state of having a metric that seems to be fluctuating?

Ries suggests we replace vanity metrics with what he calls "actionable metrics," where "data must demonstrate clear cause and effect and be related to changes" to our product, our services, or our system.[7] Otherwise, we're just randomly trying a bunch of improvements, and that's no way to run a business.

One classic example of a vanity metric is the number of visitors that come to a website. This number is easily measured, and we would hope to see a trend that increases, always going "up and to the right," as entrepreneurs often say. But, higher website traffic-numbers might be meaningless if that does not translate into increased sales. What's easy to measure isn't always what's meaningful to our business.

Other examples of vanity metrics might include the number of "Lean Six Sigma Green Belts" we have trained or certified or the number of improvements and projects that are completed. Those are easy to count, but it's also too easy to lose focus on the measures that matter, such as quality, market share, and profit.

As Ries wrote in his second book, *The Startup Way*:

> "The fact that your site has seen an uptick in visitors doesn't mean your product is more popular or you're more successful."[8]

KaiNexus, a startup I have worked with, does measure website traffic. But, more important metrics include profit, which is driven by revenue, which is driven by sales, which are converted from qualified leads, that often start as website visitors.

If KaiNexus lost sight of the real objective, they could publish really popular "clickbait" type articles that might attract a large audience. Instead, the company's inbound marketing process is designed to attract people who are likely to pursue buying their type of software.

The Dangers of Arbitrary and Unachievable Targets

Where we see a metric, we usually see a target. That's the reality of modern organizations. Leaders spend a lot of time debating whether this year's target should be something really specific, such as the possibly insignificant difference between 34.17 and 34.634.

As an aside, some people use the words "goal" and "target" interchangeably. In this book, we'll adopt the other convention that says a goal is a longer-term ideal objective, such as the goal of "zero preventable harm" in a hospital, while a target is shorter term and helps us gauge progress toward the ultimate goal.

I've seen too many cases where an organization didn't hit their target one year, only to then set the same target the next. Or, they've optimistically set an even-higher target. The implication in most organizations seems to be, "If we choose the right metrics and set challenging targets, then improvement will happen." If it were only so easy, everybody would be hitting their targets, whether that's increasing sales in a startup or reducing falls in a hospital. This is why Deming would always ask an important and challenging question: "By what method?"[9]

It's not enough to set targets and demand better results. Too many people believe that empowerment means setting aggressive targets and then leaving people alone to figure out how to meet them. Collaborating with staff doesn't mean a leader is micromanaging. Working together to improve our systems and processes will lead to better results.

In the wrong kind of organizational culture, setting arbitrary targets can become very dysfunctional. One of Deming's famous "14 points for management" reads:

> "Eliminate slogans, exhortations, and targets for the workforce asking for zero defects and new levels of productivity. Such exhortations only create adversarial relationships, as the bulk of the causes of low quality and low productivity belong to the system and thus lie beyond the power of the workforce."[10]

I've worked in the type of culture that Deming warned about. So, I understand how an "us versus them" environment creates unbearable stress when leaders demand performance that's unrealistic and then blame employees for not meeting that impossible standard.

It's not enough to set targets and demand better results.

There's a difference between an arbitrary target and one that's a "law of nature," a term used by Donald J. Wheeler, Ph.D. to describe a target that has a scientific basis, such as a 60-minute target for the "door-to-needle" time for stroke patients to get treatment. An example of an arbitrary target might be "We need to increase sales by 25% this year." A target is still arbitrary if it's based on a competitive benchmark, last year's performance, or an organizational target that has been passed down from senior leaders.

As Brian Joiner wrote in *Fourth Generation Management,* there are three things that can happen when people are pressured to hit a target without having the proper support and an effective improvement methodology. The first two are dysfunctional and are too often easier than the third, and preferred, alternative:

1. Distort the numbers
2. Distort the system
3. Improve the system[11]

We see many examples of this in the news, and we might see them in our own workplaces. In recent years, we've seen the CEO of Wells Fargo set an arbitrary target of "eight is great," meaning each customer should have eight different accounts. Since the target was unreasonable, thousands of tellers signed customers up for accounts they didn't need or didn't know about — and then got fired for being "unethical." Eventually, the CEO was forced out, into retirement.[12]

In the United States Veterans Health Administration, local clinic managers were put under pressure to keep waiting times for patients under 14 days. Even though the Congressional Budget Office called the target "unrealistic," people in dozens of offices created secret waiting lists (a paper waiting list to get on the official waiting list in the computer) or other such distortions to make results look better than they were. Again, some employees and local managers were fired for what were arguably very systemic problems.[13]

I recently heard a funny story about a fitness center that asked departing customers to push one of four buttons that rated their visit as one of the following:

- a very smiley face
- a somewhat smiley face
- a somewhat frowny face
- a very frowny face

The gym's manager and staff were promised an incentive if a certain number of customers hit the "very smiley" button each month. They might have feared being punished for not hitting that target. What did the employees figure out? They learned that they could hit the "very smiley face" button a few times each time they walked nearby, which boosted that metric. Problem solved?

However, it's possible to have a culture where a meaningful goal or target is shared by all. An organization like that tends to have supportive leaders and a spirit of "we're all in it together." Effective managers don't just set targets; they work together with people to hit those targets.

Paul O'Neill, former CEO of Alcoa, set an audacious goal for an important measure: zero employee harm in their workplaces around the world. Such a goal could have been demoralizing if it seemed impossible, and people feared punishment. However, his leadership style made it clear that accountability started with him and that the company would work together toward that ideal, without blaming or punishing anyone for not reaching that ideal target. During his tenure as CEO, Alcoa reduced "lost workdays per injury per 100 workers" from 1.86 to 0.2 (a reduction of 89%). After O'Neill's retirement, thanks to the culture and methodologies that he left in place, the rate fell to 0.125 by 2012.[14]

The Questions We Should Ask About Our Numbers

If an executive tells the VP of sales, "Revenue is 10% below our target this month" or "Sales are down 5%," it's easy to say, "That's bad." But, is such a comparison meaningful?

Many organizations limit their analysis of performance to simple comparisons to a goal, target, or budget. Or, a metric is compared to a previous time period or against an average. What does that tell us? Not much — and not enough to improve.

Let's look at one metric that's tracked by a health clinic laboratory and medical office team: the percentage of urinalysis test results that have been completed and received prior to the patient's appointment with their provider.

If we post a single data point on a whiteboard, as illustrated below, it might be obvious that we didn't meet the target this week. We can only color code data points as bad (red) or good (green). A single data point doesn't mean we can determine anything about trends, and it doesn't tell us how to improve.

The lab manager might tell the team, "Our percentage dropped from 66% to 49% last week." What does the context of a second data point tell us? Can we draw solid conclusions about performance trends?

I propose three high-level questions that are helpful, if not necessary, for improvement:

> Question 1: Are we achieving our target or goal?
> Question 2: Are we improving?
> Question 3: How do we improve?

Hopefully, this book will help you decide that all three questions are important and deserve attention.

To answer **Question 1** in this case, we are currently not hitting the target, or at least we did not meet our target in either of the last two weeks. Does this mean we can ever hit the target without taking some drastic action? We can't answer that question without additional data and the right analysis. If we were currently hitting the target, we still might have interest in reaching even-higher levels of performance, which requires answers to our next questions.

The second data point was lower than the first. Does that mean that it's going to keep going down, or is the metric fluctuating within some range? We can't tell how our performance is trending with a simple whiteboard, scoreboard, or dashboard that displays just a data point or two. *Question 2* is important since improvement is necessary when we are not meeting our target. Improvement might be desirable even when targets are being met.

> **Effective managers don't just set targets; they work together with people to hit those targets.**

Having just one or two data points doesn't help us know where to get started in answering *Question 3*. Was one of those data points an outlier, or were they both within the typical range? Being able to answer that question helps us know when we should react and investigate with urgency and when we should step back to take a more measured and systematic approach to improvement, as we'll discuss in Chapter 4. There are times when we're hitting our target some or most of the time, so we still need to know how to improve.

The methods in this book will help us make better decisions about charts and metrics. We'll be able to draw better cause-and-effect connections between our improvement efforts and our results. Moreover, we'll waste less of our valuable time since we'll stop overreacting to every up and down in the metric.

We'll be able to answer more specific versions of those three core questions:

Question 1: Are we achieving our target or goal?
    a. Are we doing so occasionally?
    b. Are we doing so consistently?

Question 2: Are we improving?
    a. Can we predict future performance?

Question 3: How do we improve?
    a. When do we react?
    b. When do we step back and improve the system?
    c. How can we prove we've improved?

The aim of this book is not learning how to create charts for our metrics; it's about improving performance through these methods and these questions.

We'll waste less of our valuable time since we'll stop overreacting to every up and down in the metric.

Measuring and Managing Personal or Organizational Health

Let's look at a personal measurement (and management) challenge that might sound familiar. Can you represent and measure your health with a single metric? Probably not. Let's say "fitness" is your high-level objective. That's difficult to measure directly, and it's not a single number. We might decide that weight is more easily measured, and we have a hypothesis that says lower weight equals better fitness, which would then lead to better health, better quality of life, and a longer life.

Others might choose a handful of what we could call "process metrics" that include weight, body-fat percentage, blood pressure, and total cholesterol. Others might choose different metrics that are more relevant to their own health, conditions, and risks. A balanced scorecard that represents one's health can prevent the dysfunctions that can result from focusing too much on any one metric.

For each metric, we (or a doctor) would typically set a target. If there is a gap between our current performance and the target, we work to close that gap through various forms of improvement activity. Hopefully, we are going about that in a systematic way instead of randomly trying different solutions or quick fixes. *→ Patient Experience, Throughput, etc*

Weight is just a number. I don't manage the number; I do what I can to manage the system (including diet and exercise) that leads to the number (*results*). There are also factors that I can't control, such as genetics or environmental factors.

The word "results" should remind us that any metric is the *result* of some work, process, or system. In a workplace, our "process measures," such as the number of new marketing contacts generated each day in sales, should lead to a "results measure" of new customers, revenue, or profit. This brings us to our first key point:

**KEY POINT #1: We don't manage the metric; we manage
the system that leads to the results, and we lead
the people who help us improve the system.**

As I've learned, working out three times a week with a trainer might lead to a net weight *gain* that occurs as the result of losing fat and adding muscle. One might be troubled if our high-level aim was defined only as weight. But, somebody aiming for fitness or health as an objective might readily accept a higher weight, especially when one's pants fit better and the heart is performing more efficiently.

A few years back, my weight approached 200 pounds for the first time. I identified a gap between my current weight and a target of 185 pounds (it was admittedly arbitrary and not based on science). Measurement was important, but I also learned not to overreact to every small fluctuation in my weight. I learned to weigh myself at a consistent time each day to eliminate the effect of how weight naturally fluctuates during the day. I improved my own personal system (exercising more and using an app to track calories) and reached my target over a few months.

I learned to look at my weight as a range of numbers that naturally fluctuates a bit from day to day instead of thinking of it as a single number that always had to remain the same. Small fluctuations didn't cause alarm, but larger changes would ideally draw more attention (and analysis of how my diet or exercise had changed).

It can be difficult to sustain an improved system. Case in point, my weight over time has crept back up to 200 pounds for a variety of reasons. The answer to why my weight increased again can't be answered by asking, "What went wrong yesterday (or last week)?" It's more related to patterns and changes in behavior over time. Maybe I can blame aging and metabolism.

I've demonstrated that I know how to lose weight. Why didn't I take corrective action when my weight went up to 190? Why am I reacting again only now that I'm back at 200? I had stopped measuring my weight, perhaps due to being on the road too much and then being in denial about my weight creeping back up. Choosing not to look at a metric isn't a good strategy for improvement.

If managing one's own personal system is difficult, think of how much more challenging this is in an organization — not just improving performance but also sustaining the gains. How often do we let an organizational metric get really bad before we respond and ask questions about improvement? How can we manage more effectively?

Reducing Waste Through "Lean"

Time is a precious commodity. Leaders, including startup founders, nurse managers, and plant managers, all have to make constant choices about how to allocate their limited time and attention. Urgent (but hopefully proverbial) fires pop up regularly, data gets thrown at us, and we're expected to respond. You might be told, "Don't just sit there — do something!"

How often do our choices about when and how to react end up consuming more of our time, to little real benefit? Does a series of non-stop reactive, knee-jerk responses to changes in performance metrics help us reach our goals?

I've spent almost 25 years studying and practicing the "Lean" management methodology. Toyota is considered the originator of Lean, but these methods and mindsets are being used in healthcare and many other workplaces. Toyota has long emphasized that we should reduce the "waste of motion," as one of the "eight types of waste."[15] With Lean, we aim to improve efficiency and flow by reducing waste, interruptions, defects, and delays, instead of focusing on doing the actual work more quickly. We can do more with less without overburdening people.

This applies to factory workers, nurses, and other frontline employees in any workplace. We can also reduce waste in knowledge work. Wasted motion can occur even when we're sitting in a chair, thinking, typing, or moving our mouse. The idea also applies to leaders. Meetings are held, lines are drawn on charts, data points are circled, solutions are offered. But, how often does this activity turn out to be a different type of waste? This management waste might be more difficult to see than the waste in physical work, but it also might be more damaging to an organization.

Ries wrote, in *The Lean Startup,* about how wasteful it is to have software developers spend years working on software that doesn't get purchased by customers after it's finally released. He asked a very important question at the end of the book, something that's both a matter of respect and organizational performance:

"If we stopped wasting people's time, what would they do with it?"[16]

That time can be better used for more productive activities that better serve our customers and lead to more success for ourselves and our organizations.

We can do more with less without overburdening people.

The methods in this book will help you save time by teaching you when and how to react (or not react) to changes in metrics, allowing you to focus your efforts on important and necessary improvement activity.

How Do We Manage Our Metrics?

For my consulting company, is the number of visitors to my blog a vanity metric, particularly since I don't make much money from advertising or other revenue streams that correlate directly to more people reading my blog?

Metrics that are more important for my business include the number of new consulting or speaking clients. Higher blog traffic might help further that goal. I can't prove, statistically, that months with higher blog traffic result in more speaking and consulting work. That might be a function of the *quality* of my posts (or other factors that are in or out of my control).

Assuming blog traffic does matter, how would I go about best managing that metric? When we look at metrics the wrong way, it's too easy to draw an incorrect conclusion, one that leads to an unrealistic view of our current situation. Or, it's often too easy to intentionally distort or cherry pick numbers to tell the story we want to tell.

In the case of website metrics, we could modify the Ries quote to say something slightly different but still important:

> **"The fact that your site has seen an uptick in visitors this week doesn't mean your website is getting more visitors consistently over time."**

Google Analytics sends me an email each month that shows a comparison of two data points related to my blog, www.LeanBlog.org. It presents the number of users with a comparison to the previous month, as shown below:

June performance for your website vs. previous month

Users

16.4K ↓21.83%

I can log in to Google Analytics to find a month that shows a nice percentage increase in a metric, like the number of page views. I can illustrate this below in the type of table we often see in management reports or slide decks (these reports often place the newest numbers to the left, which seems confusing):

	April 2017	March 2017	April 2016
Page Views	64,481	46,625	42,729
Percentage Chage From Previous Period		38.6%	50.9%

I might say, "Hooray, an increase of almost 40% from last month! Up 50% since last year!" I'm rounding up, of course, to paint an even better picture of progress.

How do I know the number hadn't *decreased* by a similar amount the month before? Comparing any two data points doesn't provide enough information for me to understand my system and to properly evaluate trends in its performance.

KEY POINT #2: Two data points are not a trend.

Thankfully, I don't have investors or an executive whom I'm trying to con-vince that 40% improvement is going to happen every month. I'd only be fooling myself to think so, and doing that doesn't help improve my business. Ries always warns against creating "success theater."

One form of "success theater" is using or displaying metrics in a way that makes performance look better than it is. As Ries wrote, "Energy invested in suc-cess theater is energy that could have been used to build a sustainable business."[17] Another form of success theater would be unethical tactics that artificially boost the number of page loads (an example of the distortions that Joiner warned about).

> "The fact that your site has seen an uptick in visitors this week doesn't mean your website is getting more visitors consistently."

After the 38.6% increase in April, the May traffic number shows a 38.7% decline from the month before:

	May 2017	April 2017	May 2016
Page Views	39,517	64,481	40,039
Percentage Chage From Previous Period		-38.7%	-1.3%

Well, so much for that trend I might have hoped for. My blog traffic came back down to earth or regressed to the mean, perhaps. I could emphasize that the drop from May 2016 was very small.

These numbers tell me something (but not much) about the past. What could I expect to see for blog traffic in the future? Can I better understand past perfor-mance in a way that predicts future performance? Yes, by using a "Process Behavior Chart," which will be introduced in the next chapter.

Comparing two data points means we are missing a lot of context, including the other months' data and the trends we might see by looking at more data.

As Wheeler wrote in *Understanding Variation*:

KEY POINT #3: "No data have meaning apart from their context."[18]

If comparing two numbers isn't very helpful, organizations often try to provide additional context by displaying tables with many numbers on bulletin boards or electronic dashboards.

It's very difficult for people to see trends in a table of numbers, the way some of my blog data is shown below. This style of presenting a metric over time is sometimes called a "scorecard." Or, it's often referred to as a "Bowling Chart" because it's like the grid you'd use to keep score when going bowling, with numbers going from left to right.

Jan-16	Feb-16	Mar-16	Apr-16	May-16	Jun-16	Jul-16	Aug-16	Sep-16	Oct-16	Nov-16	Dec-16
48074	43519	42518	42749	40039	37336	30454	37670	35860	36817	37919	32542

Jan-17	Feb-17	Mar-17	Apr-17	May-17	Jun-17	Jul-17	Aug-17	Sep-17	Oct-17	Nov-17	Dec-17
50241	45044	44493	60373	37152	29048	29361	30899	30532	34912	31796	24222

Is my blog traffic increasing or decreasing? It's hard to tell. The best we can usually do is to compare a point to the previous year or to the same month in the previous year. We might look at the first few data points and the last few — but there's a risk that we might draw the wrong conclusion from this visualization of the data.

Sometimes, these Bowling Charts have color coding that compares each month's data point to a target, as shown below. Data points that are better than a target are shaded green, while months that miss the target are shaded red.

True North Pillar	Metric	Desired Direction		Jan-16	Feb-16	Mar-16	Apr-16	May-16	Jun-16	Jul-16	Aug-16	Sep-16	Oct-16	Nov-16	Dec-16
Quality & Safety	Falls with Severe Injury	DOWN	Actual	0	1	0	0	1	0	0	0	0			
			Target	0	0	0	0	0	0	0	0	0	0	0	0
Quality & Safety	CLABSI	DOWN	Actual	0	0	1	0	0	1	2	0	0			
			Target	0	0	0	0	0	0	0	0	0	0	0	0
Quality & Safety	CAUTI	DOWN	Actual	1	0	0	0	0	0	0	1	1			
			Target	0	0	0	0	0	0	0	0	0	0	0	0
Team Engagement	Necessary Information Available Survey	UP	Actual	67.3%	50.8%	48.3%	70.4%	46.9%	40.6%	61.3%	70.5%	50.9%			
			Target	80.0%	80.0%	80.0%	80.0%	80.0%	80.0%	80.0%	80.0%	80.0%	80.0%	80.0%	80.0%
Patient Experience	Likelihood to recommend	UP	Actual	76.4%	78.4%	80.5%	70.0%	46.0%	40.0%	60.0%	70.0%	50.0%			
			Target	79.9%	79.9%	79.9%	79.9%	79.9%	79.9%	79.9%	79.9%	79.9%	79.9%	79.9%	79.9%
Patient Experience	Hospital rating	UP	Actual	76.4%	77.7%	77.6%	77.6%	77.2%	77.6%	77.0%	75.0%	63.0%			
			Target	77.5%	77.5%	77.5%	77.5%	77.5%	77.5%	77.5%	77.5%	77.5%	77.5%	77.5%	77.5%

A red/green Bowling Chart answers *Question 1*: "Are we meeting our targets?" We might try to answer *Questions 1a* and *1b*, "Are we meeting our targets occasionally or consistently?" by counting the number of green and red boxes.

The Bowling Chart doesn't easily answer *Question 2*: "Are we improving?" We might vaguely determine we're getting better if we see more red to the left of the chart and more green to the right. But how can we tell if those changes are significant and sustainable? How can we predict future performance?

Additionally, this binary good-or-bad analysis does not help us answer *Questions 3a* and *3c* about "When do we react?" and "How will we know if we improve?" Which, if any, of those red numbers represent something worth reacting to?

When presented with a Bowling Chart with a large number of metrics, the red and green color coding doesn't help us prioritize our investigation and improvement efforts. What if six of our 10 metrics are red right now? Does each of those merit the same response? Which metric has the biggest gap between target and actual? Does a metric going from green to red over time mean that anything has changed in the underlying system?

What if all 10 metrics on the scorecard are green? Does that mean we have unchallenging targets? Does "all green" mean there's no need for problem solving or improvement? Does a metric remaining green mean that nothing has changed or that nothing is degrading in the process? We'll come back to these questions in Chapter 4.

Graphs Are More Helpful Than Numbers

A graph or a chart is a much more effective way of making sense of data and metrics. A chart is pictorial, and our human brain processes images much better than lists of numbers. Watch a cable business channel and you'll see they usually show a graph of a company's stock performance over time instead of a table of numbers showing the stock price on different days. Unfortunately, their scroll at the bottom of the screen shows a constant stream of two-data-point comparisons of a stock's price compared to yesterday.

There's no technological excuse for bombarding people with tables of numbers instead of presenting a chart. Charts are easy to produce with modern technology. We can even use very old "technology" to draw them by hand. The Bowling Chart shown above could be replaced with six graphs that would give much more information about trends to the consumer of that data. Six graphs would take up more space on a bulletin board but would help a leader and their team save time and improve more.

When given two data points, such as "blog traffic is higher this month," drawing a Run Chart to visualize that limited data set isn't very helpful, either, as we see below:

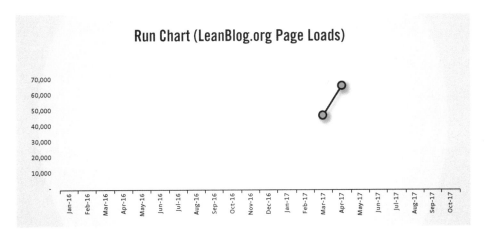

We're missing important context that tells us if the difference between those numbers is routine or exceptional. How much do the numbers normally change from month to month? All we know from this treatment of the data is that the April 2017 number is higher than it was in March 2017.

Even saying that April is 39% higher than March doesn't provide much context, since we don't know if it normally fluctuates that much month to month. It's possible that a large percentage change is not statistically significant; it's also conceivable that a small percentage change would be significant in a different metric and situation.

KEY POINT #4: A chart will always tell us more than a list of numbers.

A Run Chart tells us much more than two numbers or a table of many numbers, as seen below:

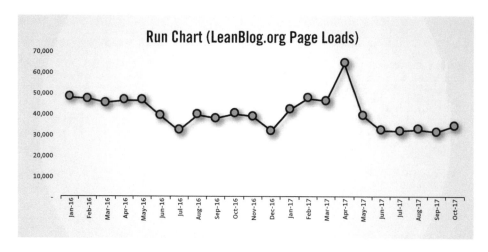

As you learn and practice this methodology, I hope you'll challenge others when they present two data points or a simple before-and-after comparison. You can ask them to "plot the dots," as some professionals from the National Health Service in England say, using the Twitter hashtag #plotthedots.[19]

What do you see? What does the chart tell you?

The Run Chart tells the honest story that my blog traffic fluctuates from month to month. The Bowling Chart tries to tell us the same thing, but it's much easier to hear what Deming and Wheeler call "the voice of the process" when we allow a chart to speak to us.

Alternatively, the "voice of the customer" tells us what is required, such as a specification or target. We hope the voice of the process tells us that our system is capable of meeting those needs all of the time. If not, we need to improve.

> **"It's much easier to hear the voice of the process when we allow a chart to speak to us."**

Thinking back to the whiteboard and the urinalysis metric from earlier in this chapter, a Run Chart conveys much more context and information:

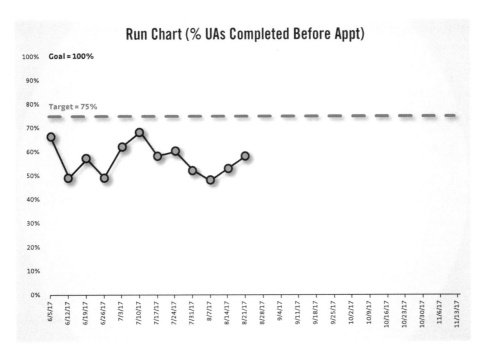

The chart shows the target and 12 weeks of data. We can answer **Question 1** a little better now. It appears we have never reached our target, and it seems unlikely to happen unless we can improve the system that produces those results. We can try to answer **Question 2** by saying that the metric seems to be fluctuating — some weeks are better than others. Does this chart help us answer **Question 3** about how to react and improve? Not really.

The same system, with the same people doing the same work in the same situation, will not always produce the exact same results each day, each week, or each month. This is a fact of life — there's always variation in a metric. This was true in my blog traffic, and it was true in the urinalysis example. As Deming said, "Life is variation."[20]

The question we will answer soon is "How much variation is routine and to be expected in this particular situation?" If we discover that the variation in our metric is about the same over time and it's centered around a stable average, we then have a performance measure that allows us to predict future performance. The Process Behavior Chart methodology, to be introduced in the next chapter, helps us answer our three core questions in a way that Bowling Charts and Run Charts cannot.

KEY POINT #5: The job of management is not just to look backward but also to look forward and predict, if possible, what is likely to occur.

Metrics are most often used to look backward and to make evaluations about past performance. But, we also need to prepare for the future of our organization and its performance.

As the late MIT professor Myron Tribus said:

> **"Managing a company by means of the monthly report is like trying to drive a car by watching the yellow line in the rear-view mirror."[21]**

Glancing back at the Run Chart for my blog traffic data, it looks like the April data point is indeed a significant increase from the previous months. Before April, the metric seemed to be fluctuating around an average. Is this April increase something exceptional? Does it deserve our attention or an investigation? Do we have to guess? How would we know? As you will see in Chapter 2, the Process Behavior Chart points the way.

Summary of Key Points Introduced So Far:

KEY POINT #1: We don't manage the metric; we manage the system that leads to the results, and we lead the people who help us improve the system.

KEY POINT #2: Two data points are not a trend.

KEY POINT #3: "No data have meaning apart from their context."

KEY POINT #4: A chart will always tell us more than a list of numbers.

KEY POINT #5: The job of management is not just to look backward, but also to look forward and predict, if possible, what is likely to occur.

Three Core Questions:

Question 1: Are we achieving our target or goal?
   a.   Are we doing so occasionally?
   b.   Are we doing so consistently?

Question 2: Are we improving?
   a.   Can we predict future performance?

Question 3: How do we improve?
   a.   When do we react?
   b.   When do we step back and improve the system?
   c.   How can we prove we've improved?

CHAPTER 2

Using Process Behavior Charts for Metrics

s we saw in Chapter 1, Run Charts tell us much more than a single data point, a comparison description, or a table of numbers. The Process Behavior Chart (PBC) methodology is even more helpful since it provides a way to answer our core questions about performance and improvement. The PBC method not only tells us if we're meeting our goals or targets (***Question 1***), it also helps us say, based on three simple rules, if our metric is improving, getting worse, or just fluctuating (***Question 2***). The chart and these rules can tell us when to react and when to step back and look at improving the underlying process (***Question 3***).

The PBC tells us when the system that produces our metric has changed, for the better or the worse. It won't tell us *why* it changed, but the PBC tells us when to go investigate. The PBC method will focus our efforts, saving some of our valuable time by helping us learn when *not* to react, using our valuable time, instead, for systematic improvement.

A Process Behavior Chart is a form of what's more generally called a "Control Chart" or a "Statistical Process Control (SPC) Chart." It's also sometimes called an "Individuals Control Chart with a Moving Range." That's a mouthful.

Wheeler coined the Process Behavior Chart term, suggesting that the word "control," while intended to have a benign connotation, nevertheless has "baggage" associated with it.[22] Another argument for "Process Behavior Chart" is that it's a more accurate descriptive phrase, as the chart, well, explains the behavior of the process.

A PBC is a pairing of two specialized and related Run Charts.

The first, called the "X Chart" (or "Individuals Chart"), contains the data points from a metric. The second, the "Moving Range Chart" (or "MR Chart"), shows us the amount of point-to-point variation between each data point on the X Chart, information that is useful in a different way. The charts are designed to be used together, but using the X Chart alone can still help us greatly, and it simplifies the approach.

Our main focus, for now, is learning how to interpret PBCs that have already been created, as that's what most leaders will do. The charts might be created by analysts or improvement specialists (and Appendix A is there for them). Leaders at all levels can use this methodology to make better decisions, to save time by not reacting to every up and down in a metric and use that saved time to improve more effectively.

The X Chart

We create an X Chart by plotting our metric as we would on a Run Chart. We then also perform some simple calculations that allow us to add three very helpful horizontal lines that help us interpret the chart:

- A "Central Line" (typically the average)
- An "Upper Natural Process Limit"
- A "Lower Natural Process Limit"

The Natural Process Limits are the guardrails that tell us where a predictable metric is going to fluctuate over time — unless the system changes.

Below is an X Chart for a period of about six weeks in 2016, after my initial weight loss, when my weight fluctuated around an average. My target weight was 185, which is shown as the dashed blue line:

Leaders at all levels can use this methodology to make better decisions, to save time by not reacting to every up and down in a metric and use that saved time to improve more effectively.

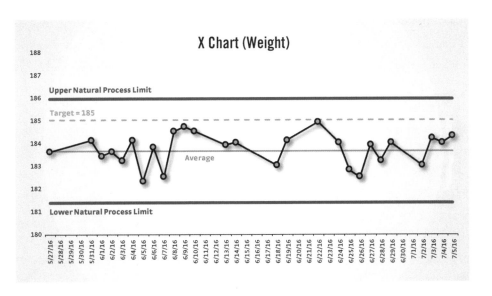

The X Chart calculations use a baseline of historical data, ideally 20 data points (or as few as six data points to create temporary limits to start). In Appendix A, you can find the detailed methodology for these calculations. After this baseline is created, future data points are evaluated against the initial average and limits.

It should be emphasized that the Natural Process Limits are *calculated*. They are not chosen by the creator of the chart. The limits should not be confused with any management targets for the metric or specifications that come from a customer.

We'll soon learn how the baseline PBC tells us if our system is "predictable" or not, using that term in a very specific way. If the PBC is a predictable system, the PBC makes useful predictions about future performance, answering *Question 2a*, something that Bowling or Run Charts cannot do. A predictable metric tends to remain predictable, unless something changes significantly in the system. In a predictable system, we'd expect future performance to fluctuate within the range of the Natural Process Limits, usually spending roughly equal time on both sides of the average.

The PBC for my weight tells me it's a predictable system. Soon, we'll learn the exact rules we use to determine if it's predictable or not. I could have expected my weight to fluctuate between about 181 and 186 pounds on any given day in the immediate future, unless something changed in the "system" that is my life and health.

The PBC methodology tells me not to automatically react to any day's weight that's above my target. The PBC tells me that my weight would remain below my target most days, but not all. A day above my target wouldn't mean I should take any drastic action or feel bad.

Understanding that a system is predictable helps us understand how to improve (*Question 3*). I wouldn't likely find improvements by asking for an explanation of any day's weight that's between the Natural Process Limits.

As we'll see, it's also possible that a metric is predictable, per the voice of the process, but it does not satisfy the needs (the target) articulated by the voice of the customer. In a situation like this, where there is a performance gap, we'd be compelled to improve.

> Leaders can use this methodology to make better decisions, to save time by not reacting to every up and down in a metric and use that saved time to improve more effectively.

It's also possible that the PBC tells us that we have an unpredictable system. As we'll discuss in Chapter 4, improving an unpredictable system requires that we first take action to stabilize the system, making it predictable, and then improving from there.

We'll also learn how, as we add data points over time, we can use the PBC to help understand if the system has changed or not. How do we know if a predictable system has become unpredictable, driven by a change in our underlying system?

As we try to improve, we can introduce a change to the system and then use the PBC to see if we then get the improved results that we expected from our change. Other times, the PBC helps us discover something has changed, and it's then our job to investigate and try to understand why.

A Process Behavior Chart for Blog Traffic

If I go back and chart my blog's traffic from August 2010 to January 2012, the X Chart portion of the PBC is seen below. We see the data, in blue, along with the calculated average and limits. In this example, I am not comparing performance to a target; I'm looking first to understand the system and the metric.

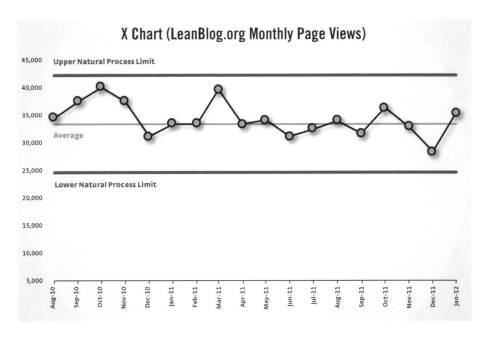

At a glance, the data seems to fluctuate around the average (the green line) without any obvious trends or patterns. What else does the X Chart say to us?

It shows me that, in some months, traffic will be higher than others. I can't expect that a complex system will generate the same results each month. The chart allows me to predict that future blog traffic will fall between about 25,000 and 43,000 page views in future months — unless something changes in the system. It's a "predictable system" that exhibits nothing but "routine variation" or what we could call "noise" in the system. But how do we know if it's predictable?

Predictable System = Noise = Routine Variation

There are three specific and scientific rules that tell us if there are any "signals" in an X Chart. We don't have to guess if the system has changed or when to react. Finding a signal through these rules is evidence of what we call "exceptional variation" — a data point (or points) unlikely to be generated by our previously predictable system. The exceptional variation is outside of the "routine variation" that normally exists.

Unpredictable System = Signals = Exceptional Variation

If we can't distinguish signal from noise, we'll end up reacting too often, wasting valuable time and hampering our improvement.

As Wheeler writes:

"While every data set contains noise, some data sets may contain signals. Before you can detect a signal within any given data set, you must first filter out the noise."[23]

As I've learned from Wheeler's work, the tool for filtering out that noise is the Process Behavior Chart.

In other words, we look for moments of exceptional variation by filtering out routine variation. When we learn not to react to routine variation, we'll free up a lot of time to react when it's appropriate and improve when it's necessary.

KEY POINT #6: There is variation in every metric or data set. Process Behavior Charts filter out noise so we can identify signals.

So how do we know exactly if our charts have signals or if we're looking at noise?

The three rules we use to identify signals in the X Chart of a PBC are:

- **Rule 1**: Any data point outside of the limits.
- **Rule 2**: Eight consecutive points on the same side of the central line.
- **Rule 3**: Three out of four consecutive data points that are closer to the same limit than they are to the central line.

How strong are each of these signals? Wheeler, in his book *Making Sense of Data,* compares the confidence we should place in the three rules. A single point outside of the limits (*Rule 1*) is a "large effect," meaning there is, with almost complete certainty, a root cause for that change. With that single data point, we don't know yet if the cause will go away (or can be eliminated) or if it's the beginning of a more sustained effect that would be identified by our other two rules. A *Rule 2* shift signifies a "moderate but sustained effect," and *Rule 3* shows a "weak but sustained effect."

My initial X Chart for blog visitor data, however, shows no signals, per these three rules. That means the metric is the result of a predictable process. Each data point on that chart can be considered to be "noise." Future results are predictable and the Natural Process Limits show us the range of future performance, which will be centered around that average.

An X Chart for a different metric, below, shows all three rules — three different signals of changes to the metric and the underlying system.

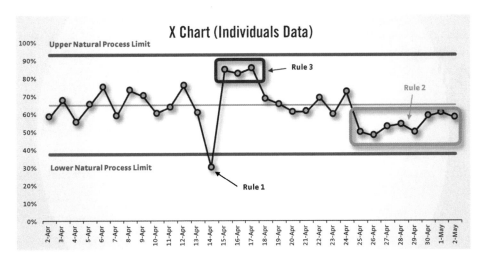

A signal tells us something has changed and that there's a "special cause" to be found. In other words, we can work to identify the root cause of a signal. The special cause leads to exceptional variation in our metric.

Unpredictable System = Signals
= Exceptional Variation = Special Cause Variation

If there is a signal that takes the chart in a positive direction, we need to understand the cause so we can make sure the change isn't temporary. If we see a signal in a negative direction, we need to identify and eliminate that special cause, so we can restore performance to previously predictable levels (or better). We need a different mindset for improving a system that has nothing but noise, as we'll discuss in Chapter 4.

Predictable System = Noise = Routine Variation
= Common Cause Variation

Again, the lack of signals in a PBC indicates we have a predictable system. In a predictable system, each data point can be considered "noise." There's no specific reason for why a particular data point is what it is. It's important not to overreact to noise. Asking "What happened last month?" rarely helps us improve a predictable system.

Routine variation always exists in a system. There might be dozens or hundreds of sources of variation, or "common causes," that always exist. For my blog, those common causes might include the topics I choose, the quality of my writing, and the extent to which posts get shared by people on social media.

> It's important not to overreact to noise. Asking, "What happened last month?" rarely helps us improve a predictable system.

Moving Ranges and the MR Chart

After creating the X Chart, we can also create a second, complementary chart that forms our complete PBC. This second chart is called the "Moving Range Chart" (or "MR Chart"). A "Moving Range" is the absolute value (meaning a positive number) of the difference between each two successive data points in the metric that's plotted on the X Chart.

The Moving Ranges and the Average Moving Range gives us an estimate of the typical point-to-point variation in a metric. The Average Moving Range is an input to the Natural Process Limit calculations for the X Chart, as detailed in Appendix A.

In general, when there is more point-to-point variation in our metric, the limits on the X Chart will be wider. We can have a system that's predictable within a very narrow range (if the MRs are small) or a system that's predictable within a wider range (if the MRs are larger).

We also calculate an "Upper Range Limit" for the MR Chart that tells us when we have a change between two data points in our metric (as shown on the X Chart) that's larger than we would normally see. The two successive data points on the X Chart might both be just within the Lower and Upper Limits, but the MR Chart tells us more directly when we have point-to-point variation that's larger than normal.

The X Chart is usually displayed above the MR Chart, with the two charts having the same x-axis, as shown below:

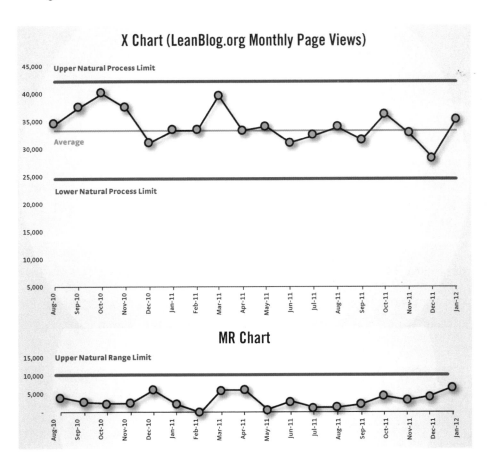

There is an additional rule for the MR Chart that we use to identify signals:

- **Rule 1**: Any data point above the MR Upper Range Limit

We see no signals in the MR Chart for blog traffic. That, combined with no signals in the X Chart, confirms that this is a predictable system over this time frame. More often than not, an X Chart with signals will have an MR Chart with signals. Only occasionally do we see an MR Chart signal without a signal on the X Chart. A signal on either chart tells us the system changed.

Using only the X Chart simplifies this methodology, while adding a small risk that we miss some signals of a changing system. Using the X Chart alone will still provide great benefits, with less risk of confusing the consumers of these charts. Throughout this book, there will be some examples that show just an X Chart and some that show both charts together.

Evaluating a Process Behavior Chart Over Time

Since the baseline for the blog traffic PBC ends with January 2012, the PBC would have allowed me to predict the number of monthly page views for February 2012 and beyond. The PBC predicts that the number will fall between the calculated Lower and Upper Limits of 25,029 and 43,510.

As time marches on, we'd look for signals (indicating a change to the system) or the lack thereof (which tells us the predictable system has remained predictable, as it's fluctuating and behaving as it had before).

Let's see what happens when we add four data points for additional months to the original PBC over time, as shown next:

Routine variation always exists in a system. There might be dozens or hundreds of sources of variation, or "common causes," that always exist.

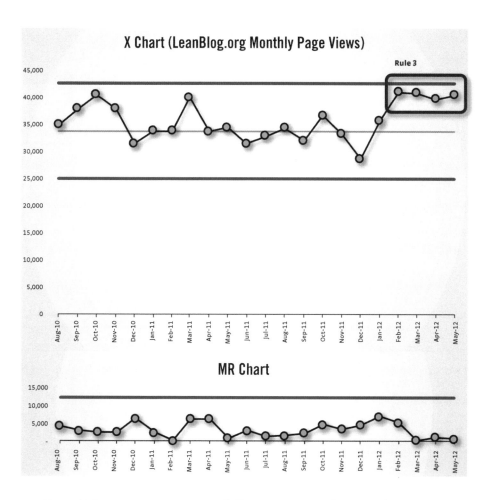

From February to May 2012, all four points are closer to the Upper Limit than they are to the average, so we have found a ***Rule 3*** signal that the system has changed.

Since this occurred six years ago, I don't know what changed in the system that led to higher traffic. This was a missed signal. The voice of the process was trying to speak to me. I didn't hear it because I wasn't plotting the PBC in real time. I don't know the cause of the increase in page views or if it was something in my control or not.

The X Chart's prediction that future months would fall between the limits was correct. One or two points near that limit wouldn't be a signal. But, we see exceptional variation in the clustering of those three consecutive points near the limit, which counts as "three out of four" for *Rule 3*. The old system wouldn't have generated those results. Something changed, and the system was, at that point, no longer predictable.

Adding additional data points through November 2013, it appears that the three-data-point increase in page views was temporary and not sustained, as shown below. The system appears to have returned to its previous state, where it was fluctuating around the baseline average. The cause of that exceptional variation has gone away. It would have been helpful to understand what led to that increase so I could have tried to sustain it, going forward. We can again predict that future performance will be between the limits.

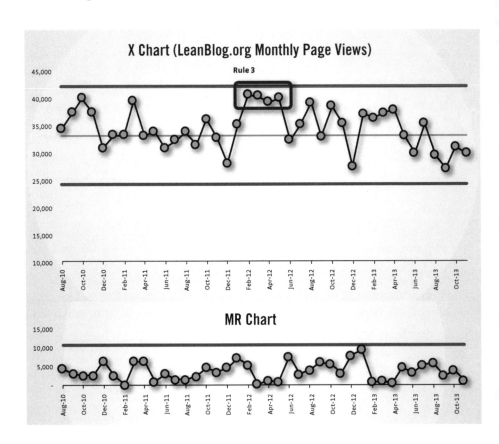

To explore what happened before the 39% increase April 2017 (as we saw in Chapter 1), I created a PBC, below, that looked back to a baseline period that starts, this time, in January 2015. This was an arbitrary starting point for the analysis, but one that gives enough historical data points for a valid baseline in terms of the average and limits. Was this a predictable system before the uptick? Was the uptick a signal?

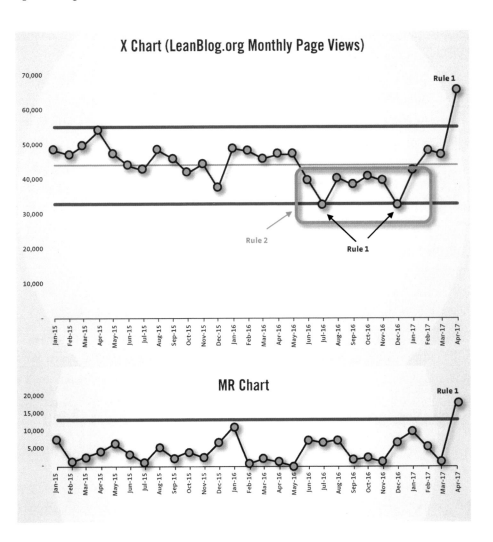

In the X Chart, we see a *Rule 1* signal above the Upper Limit and two months that were below the Lower Limit. These were July and December 2016, two months when I took breaks from blogging, which would reasonably explain the performance difference.

There is also a *Rule 2* signal, where we see a run of eight consecutive points below the average. We also see a *Rule 1* signal in the MR Chart, with a month above the calculated Upper Range Limit, which corresponds with the big increase in the X Chart. Even before the big uptick, blog traffic was not a predictable system that would give predictable results.

It appears that traffic was predictable from January 2015 until May 2016. Then, something changed, which led to a downward shift where blog traffic started fluctuating around a lower average from May 2015 until July 2016. What was the cause of that downward *Rule 2* shift?

Unfortunately, I do not have a good explanation. Online reports suggest there was a change in Google's search algorithms in June 2016, which could have affected traffic. Or, was my blog becoming less popular for other reasons? Was that a temporary downturn that corrected itself when the cause went away? A missed signal is a missed opportunity to better understand our system and to improve.

In the X Chart's last data point, we see that traffic in April jumped to 64,841. Not all upticks are created equal. This uptick is meaningful, however. That month's number is a signal (*Rule 1)* that something changed in the system. I believe the special cause here was a blog post I wrote about the passenger who was dragged off of a United Airlines flight. Because that post was written on the day of the incident, it appeared very high in search results, which led to it being read more than 26,000 times, making it my most-read post of all time.

Not all upticks are created equal.

Was this the type of special cause that would be sustained, leading to higher blog traffic every month? Would traffic now fluctuate around a new, higher average? Or would blog traffic fall back to previous levels? While I hoped people would read that United post and fall in love with Lean concepts or my blog, the reality is many of those visitors probably never returned, as I could see in the PBC that continued over time.

Unfortunately, if we look at a PBC with additional months through January 2018, the high month is followed by another eight consecutive points below the average *(Rule 2)* and many individual months below the Lower Limit (*Rule 1*):

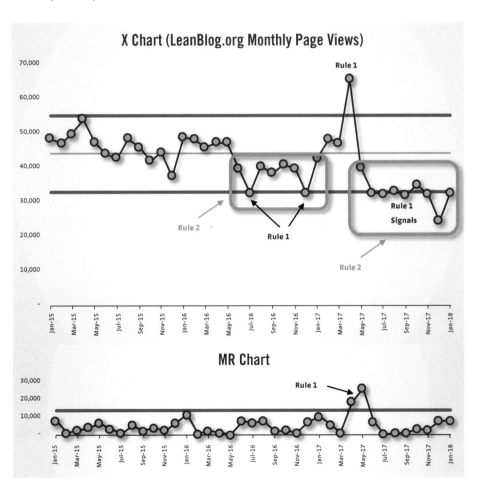

As much as I might hate to admit it, it appears the system has changed, and my blog is now fluctuating around a lower average. I doubt the blog post about United drove existing readers away. Was there another change to the Google algorithms? "What happened?" is an appropriate question when we see a signal.

It's troubling when we don't understand the causes of changes to our metrics, as it's a lost opportunity to solve a problem or to make an adjustment to our system that might put things back on track.

As we practice this PBC methodology, we'll not just make charts and update them; we'll hopefully gain a greater appreciation for cause-and-effect relationships between our systems, our improvement work, and our results, as we'll discuss in Chapter 4.

Shifting Performance

The signal means a new system has been established. This means we can calculate a new average and limits from a new baseline period, starting in May 2017, to get a revised PBC, below, that illustrates the shift downward in the metric. We can now determine if the new system's results are predictable or not.

Below, we see an X Chart with shifted limits. The new average and limits can be used to predict the future performance of this new system. In this case, the Upper Range Limit for the MR Chart did not change much.

> When do we calculate and draw new lines for the average and limits? Only do so when there is a sustained shift in the metric (usually seen through a Rule 2 signal).

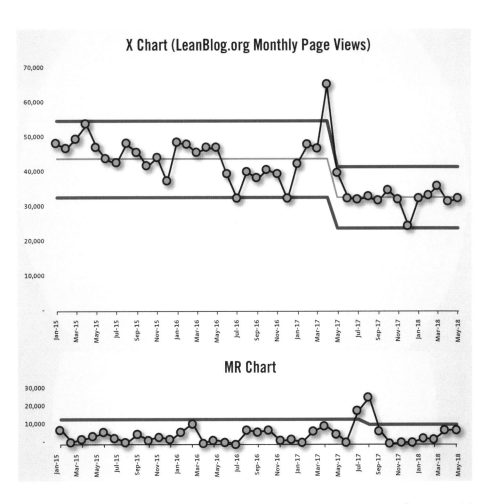

The new PBC tells me that there is a predictable system. Therefore, I could expect monthly traffic to now fall between 21,950 and 42,659 each month — unless something else changes again in the system. This is the performance I would expect regardless of the picture I might want to paint for myself, advertisers, or others.

That's how the PBC looked when I started writing this book. What happened over the next four months? How did the prediction play out?

February 2018	33,101
March 2018	35,695
April 2018	31,270
May 2018	32,296

I expect you're frustrated, at this point, by a table of numbers. You're right, it's hard to see a trend there. All four months were between the Natural Process Limits. Again, a PBC tells us more.

The updated X Chart, with those last four data points, shows the prediction was accurate:

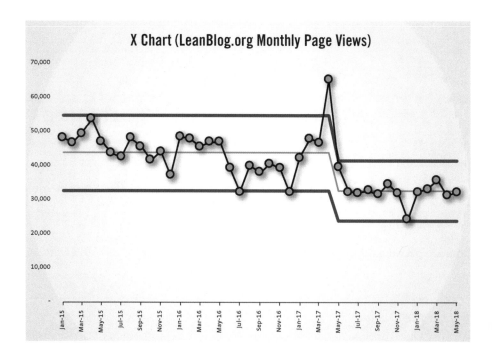

December 2017's traffic is just barely above the Lower Limit. It's technically not a signal. But, I took a lot of time off in December, which could explain the lower number.

The Longer-Term Trends

Below is a PBC that shows monthly blog traffic over a longer time period, from 2007 to 2018. What does the voice of the process say? There are signals and shifts over time. The average traffic has gone up, and it's gone down. Blog traffic has become a less predictable system over time, and the shifts seem to occur more frequently.

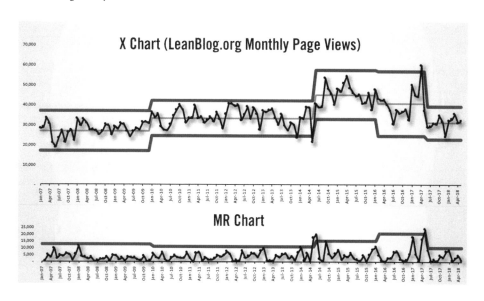

I can understand how a blog could become more popular in its early years, as the blogger builds an audience and becomes more well known. I see one shift in the chart in November 2009, which coincides with me moving my site from the Blogger platform to Wordpress. I don't know if that's correlation or causation.

In recent years, I wish I knew why the average page views fell a few times, just as any manager would want to understand what's driven increases or decreases in key metrics. The PBC tells us something has changed; it's our job to figure out why. Using PBCs in real time, with daily, weekly, or monthly data, allows us to better understand our system and improve or sustain performance.

Process Behavior Charts have helped me, and other leaders, stop reacting to every up and down in my blog traffic. Understanding this dynamic is one thing — improving a system can be more difficult. I'm just happy anyone reads the blog.

Below is a longer-term X Chart for my weight, which shows weight loss and some of what I gained back before the end of 2017:

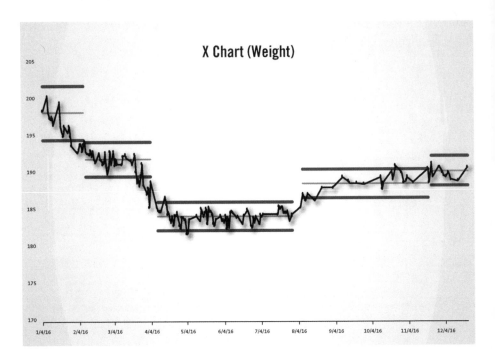

During a period of weight loss, I was happy to see that my weight was not a predictable metric. There are periods that do look like linear decline, followed by periods where my weight stabilized and fluctuated around an average. My average weight shifted downward from about 198 to 192 to 184 over a four-month period.

In August of 2016, I started traveling more, and I was weighing myself at home less frequently. In hindsight, I should have taken more corrective actions the first time I had an upward signal (a **Rule 1** signal above the Upper Limit). That was a meaningful uptick, and I should have used it as a moment to re-evaluate my eating and exercise habits. The PBC tells me something changed, as the average went up to 188. Then, there was another upward shift with a **Rule 2** run of points above that average, establishing another new system with an even-higher average.

In looking at my blog traffic or my weight, a few lessons come to mind:

- If something is important, measure it, and plot the dots.
- Tracking a metric on an ongoing basis is more helpful than using PBCs only for retrospective analysis.
- Finding signals in real time allows us to react when it's appropriate.
- PBCs tell us something has changed, but we have to figure out what changed.
- We need to figure out how to improve the system, but the PBC will help us confirm if we've made a significant impact or not.

Process Behavior Charts are helpful. Unfortunately, it can be difficult for us to change old habits about how we look at data and react. In the next chapter, we'll revisit how leaders often overreact and how the PBC method and mindset can help us react less, lead better, and improve more.

Summary of Our Rules for Evaluating PBCs:

The three rules we use to identify signals in the X Chart of a PBC are:

- **Rule 1**: Any data point outside of the limits.
- **Rule 2**: Eight consecutive points on the same side of the central line.
- **Rule 3**: Three out of four consecutive data points that are closer to the same limit than they are to the central line.

There is an additional single rule we use to identify signals in the MR Chart:

- **Rule 1**: Any data point above the MR Upper Range Limit

CHAPTER 3

Action Metrics, Not Overreaction Metrics

While Eric Ries advocates for what he calls "action metrics," I've seen far too many organizations fall into the trap and habit of what I call "overreaction metrics." When leaders overreact to every up and down in the metrics, it creates pressure on the organization, which might lead to a lot of activity that is more busy than useful. Leaders should be helping reduce waste in the organization, not adding more waste in the name of attempted improvement.

In the case of my blog traffic, I've learned not to overreact to every up and down; it's the signals (as detected by the three rules) that are worth reacting to. If I'm not happy with the average performance of the system, I can try to improve the underlying system in some way (such as improving the quality of blog posts or choosing topics that more readers care about) to try to boost that average.

But, improving the average requires efforts that are more systematic than reactive. "How can we improve the system and its typical performance?" takes us down a different path than "What went wrong last week?" It is appropriate to ask "What was different last week?" when we see a *Rule 1* signal, with a data point outside of the limits. The Natural Process Limits are calculated in a way that tells us a point outside the limits is not likely to be randomly occurring as the result of a predictable system.

However, leaders often err by reacting to every change in a metric, asking for explanations and root causes that do not exist. We shouldn't make up rules that don't have a good scientific basis, such as reacting anytime we have two consecutive points below a target.

> When leaders overreact to every up and down in the metrics,
> it creates pressure on the organization, which might lead
> to a lot of activity that is more busy than useful.

What follows is a situation that I've seen play out in many organizations, whether we're charting a manufacturing productivity metric, a patient satisfaction score, or a startup's marketing numbers. It is, in many ways, a cautionary tale about the problems that can be caused by traditional management methods.

In this scenario, a web-based software company is interested in their number of "New Premium User Registrations." Since this number drives revenue and long-term success for the company, we wouldn't consider this to be a "vanity metric."

The CEO decides that she wants or needs performance to be higher (to boost revenue and profit), so she sets a target of 90. There were 86 new premium users in the first week. This result is evaluated by the CEO as "red," since it is below the target she set.

How is this result visualized? In some workplaces, the team gets only a single data point to evaluate at a time, with no history that can be used to look for trends. A leader might write a single data point on a whiteboard that gets erased and replaced each day or week, perhaps using a red or green marker to indicate if they are hitting their target or not. A single data point, however, doesn't help us see trends or detect changes to the system.

Realizing that more data should be more helpful, the CEO posts a blank Bowling Chart template on their board to be filled in each week. The team plans on getting together weekly, huddling around the board that displays this metric.

With a Bowling Chart, each data point answers *Question 1* of "Are we achieving our target?" at the moment but does little to answer *Question 2* — "Are we improving?" The metric could shift from red to green through a small fluctuation that's noise — and not a signal.

Keep in mind, also, that the determination of "red" or "green" is completely dependent on the target that we've chosen (or was dictated to us). One way to ensure a lot of green is to set targets that aren't challenging.

Back to our patient satisfaction scenario, our Bowling Chart starts off looking like this with a single data point:

Metric	Week 1	Week 2	Week 3	Week 4	Week 5	Week 6
Registrations	86					
Target	90	90	90	90	90	90

The CEO communicates the target and encourages the team to do better next week, assuming their effort (or lack thereof) is the main factor that determines performance. The team shrugs and goes back to doing their work the way they've always done things.

Metric	Week 1	Week 2	Week 3	Week 4	Week 5	Week 6
Registrations	86	91				
Target	90	90	90	90	90	90

The team reconvenes and sees a new data point on the Bowling Chart that's colored green, since it's above the target.

The CEO praises the team. "Way to go! Keep it up!" she says. The CEO pats herself on the back subtly for creating an inspiring target that, she thinks, drove results (when we could be looking at routine variation in the metric). The team members look at each other and wonder why they're getting praised this week when it seems like they were working just as diligently as the week before, but they'll take it.

In Week 3, the result is lower and back into the red:

Metric	Week 1	Week 2	Week 3	Week 4	Week 5	Week 6
Registrations	86	91	87			
Target	90	90	90	90	90	90

This time, the CEO was too busy to come to the huddle, but she had the time beforehand to circle the 87 and scribble "Please explain!" on the sheet. She also grumbles a bit to herself about how the team must have slacked off and taken their eye off the ball after the previous week's praise.

If the team members were being honest, they'd say they have no more of an explanation for Week 3's red data point than they had for Week 2's green. They had their heads down, doing their work the same way as they had done in previous weeks, and results fluctuated.

Even though there is no clear explanation, the VP of sales scrambles and goes looking for an answer that, at the least, will sound plausible to the CEO. It only took a few seconds for the CEO's "Please explain" note. But how much time then gets wasted as a result, in meetings, discussions, deeper dives into the data and surveys — all with the purpose of coming up with an answer to the "Please explain?" This is done in the name of placating the CEO, but does this help us improve performance? Again, these explanations paint a picture that might not be our real reality. Wheeler has a colorful term for these explanations — he calls it "writing fiction."

KEY POINT #7: Don't waste time explaining noise in a metric. There is no simple, single "root cause" for noise.

Two more weeks go by with the metric getting a bit better, but it's still in the red, as posted on the board:

Metric	Week 1	Week 2	Week 3	Week 4	Week 5	Week 6
Registrations	86	91	87	87.5	89	
Target	90	90	90	90	90	90

The CEO comes to the next huddle and proclaims, "We don't want to be red, but at least things are getting better. The number is going up. I like this trend. Keep up the good progress!" She never did follow up about an answer to her question about Week 3. Life is busy, so these things tend to be forgotten (which takes pressure off those trying to come up with explanations).

Week 6 brings what might appear to the CEO to be a breakthrough with, finally, some performance that beats the target:

Metric	Week 1	Week 2	Week 3	Week 4	Week 5	Week 6
Registrations	86	91	87	87.5	89	92
Target	90	90	90	90	90	90

The CEO comes back to the team huddle and praises them for what she calls a turnaround in performance and encourages them to, again, keep it up. One of the team members wonders to himself, "Did we get better or a bit lucky last week?"

After two more weeks of green performance, the team sees this:

Metric	Week 1	Week 2	Week 3	Week 4	Week 5	Week 6	Week 7	Week 8
Registrations	86	91	87	87.5	89	92	94	92.5
Target	90	90	90	90	90	90	90	90

"We've turned the corner," says the CEO as she thinks about further inspiring the team by increasing the target to 95. In her view, setting a target led to better performance, so why not try it again? She is "raising the bar," or at least trying to. It's well intended, but is it effective? But, she's busy, and the target doesn't get updated on the board. In her mind, she knows better performance is possible — but Deming would ask "by what method?" Is the CEO going to help improve the system with her employees? Or is she merely demanding better effort?

A week later, bad news arrives — red! The number is worse than the target! The sort of analysis is very easy to do (unless you're red-green color blind), as we ask, "is it better than the target or not?"

Metric	Week 1	Week 2	Week 3	Week 4	Week 5	Week 6	Week 7	Week 8	Week 9
Registrations	86	91	87	87.5	89	92	94	92.5	87
Target	90	90	90	90	90	90	90	90	90

The CEO takes a deep breath and tells the team, "This is unacceptable. You've proven it's possible to beat the target. Look, you did it three weeks in a row. Let's do better!"

Another week goes by, and the metric returns to the green:

Metric	Week 1	Week 2	Week 3	Week 4	Week 5	Week 6	Week 7	Week 8	Week 9	Week 10
Registrations	86	91	87	87.5	89	92	94	92.5	87	95
Target	90	90	90	90	90	90	90	90	90	90

"Wow, I really lit a fire under them," the CEO tells herself. She tells the team, "That's our best performance yet! Way to go! I knew you could do it!" She circles the green number and writes "Great job!" on the paper. She also thinks, "See, I knew 95 was possible if I inspired them properly. I'll update that target soon."

The team, perhaps, realizes that this all might be something we can call "improvement theater." The CEO talks a lot about results without really doing much, yet takes credit for each improvement and blames the team for each decline.

A week later, the team huddles to find this number being posted. Again, it's red:

Metric	Week 1	Week 2	Week 3	Week 4	Week 5	Week 6	Week 7	Week 8	Week 9	Week 10	Week 11
Registrations	86	91	87	87.5	89	92	94	92.5	87	95	86
Target	90	90	90	90	90	90	90	90	90	90	90

"That's the biggest drop in performance that I can remember," says the CEO to the team. "I'm going to have to hold you accountable if things don't improve," she exclaims as she walks off toward another meeting. The team isn't sure what exactly she means by "accountable," but what they hear is, "I'll blame you if performance is low again."

The team is discouraged as Week 12 is posted:

Metric	Week 1	Week 2	Week 3	Week 4	Week 5	Week 6	Week 7	Week 8	Week 9	Week 10	Week 11	Week 12
Registrations	86	91	87	87.5	89	92	94	92.5	87	95	86	85
Target	90	90	90	90	90	90	90	90	90	90	90	90

A team (and its leaders) will get worn out on this red/green rearview-mirror style of reactive management. Instead of spending time reacting to each up and down or reacting to every point that's above or below an arbitrary target, can we manage in a way that helps us answer **Question 2** about "Are we improving?" Are we getting better? Or worse? Are we staying the same? Can we predict future performance?

When we look at a Run Chart for these 12 weeks, as shown below, it starts becoming more apparent that we have a metric that appears to be fluctuating around an average that happens to be close to the target.

This particular Run Chart chart also illustrates the swings in emotion that we often see in situations like this, in what I call "Management by Emoji":

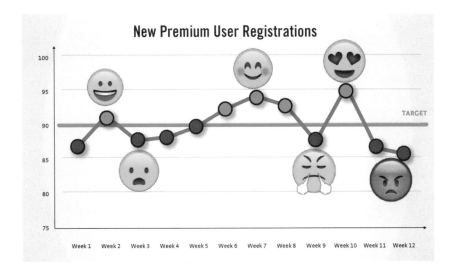

Over time, performance appears to be getting neither better nor worse. Each data point seems to be noise in the metric. The reactions, positive or negative, along with any sort of color coding, are wasted time and energy.

You might say, "But if we're not always hitting our target, we need to improve!"

Yes, of course. But, the way we improve a system that's fluctuating in performance is through less reactive means than asking, "What went wrong that week?" or "What went well that week?"

Think again about a personal metric like your weight. Fitness experts say that we need to be careful about overreacting to every number we see on the scale. Our weight naturally fluctuates by a few pounds over the course of the day, so the time we weigh ourselves is one of many factors that contributes to routine variation. Other common cause variables might include our level of hydration, the climate, and our exercise routines.

If we're trying to maintain a stable weight, we probably shouldn't stress out over our weight being 0.4 pounds higher than the previous day. We probably shouldn't necessarily ask, "Why do I weigh more?" from that single data point. We might want to ask that question if we see a more meaningful trend over time. And, again, Process Behavior Charts can help us understand when to react or not overreact.

As Deming said:

> **"Management must understand the theory of variation: If you don't understand variation and how it comes from the system itself, you can only react to every figure.**
>
> **The result is you often overcompensate, when it would have been better to just leave things alone."**[24]

Even better than leaving things alone is working together to improve.

Replacing Our Bowling Chart With a Process Behavior Chart

To create a PBC, we take our premium user registration data and simply plot the dots in a Run Chart with the average that was calculated from these 12 data points. The average is part of what the "voice of the process" is telling us — the expected average performance that we'll continue to see if we have a predictable system with predictable results, regardless of whether the system meets the target or not.

The average of 89.3 happens to be slightly less than the target of 90. This often happens when an organization sets a target that is similar to the previous year's performance in a predictable system.

With a PBC, the points on the chart aren't color coded red and green, since we're moving away from the simple focus on comparing each data point to the target. Instead of focusing on each individual point as a special event, our aim is to increase the average performance level so that, even with our variation and fluctuations, the metric is always better than the target — and, hopefully, continues to improve.

Our next step allows us to see the difference between routine variation and exceptional variation — the difference between noise and signal.

We calculate and add the Upper Natural Process Limit and the Lower Natural Process Limit, lines that are symmetrical around the average. Again, you can jump to Appendix A to learn how to calculate the limits. For now, we'll start by focusing on how to use and interpret PBCs.

Remember, these limits are *calculated* from our baseline data; you do not get to choose the limits the way you might choose a goal or a desired range of performance. The Natural Process Limits are also part of the "voice of process" in that they tell us how much variation is to be expected unless something changes in the system.

A PBC for the number of new premium users is shown below:

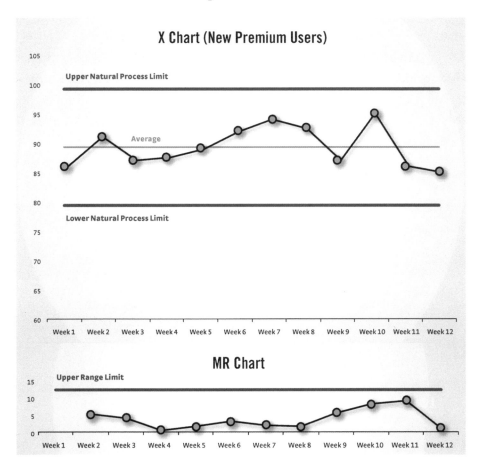

In this X Chart, we see no signals. There are no signals in the MR Chart. The lack of signals shows we have a predictable system, with nothing but noise or routine variation. There's nothing that happened in any particular week that's worth investigating in a reactive "What happened?" way. The same system that generates 86 new users in a week might sometimes also generate 95 new users. This is part of the inherent variation in our system.

The Natural Process Limits are calculated in a way that filters out almost all noise in a metric (see Appendix A). Having a predictable system means that we can predict, with good confidence, that we'll have between 79.4 (the Lower Limit) and 99.25 (the Upper Limit) new premium user registrations. Some weeks, we'll have more than 89.3 (the average), and some weeks we'll have less. We might even have a few consecutive weeks above or below our average, which could be due to chance. Therefore, we shouldn't overreact about that or declare that we see trends that might not be valid. Use the three rules. We also shouldn't try to explain every up and down when there is no single root cause for that noise.

As weeks tick by, we add more data points to the Process Behavior Chart.

Let's say, in Week 13, the number is below the Lower Limit. We also see an MR point above the Upper Range Limit. This shows there is a signal worth investigating because something has changed in our system.

> The lack of signals shows we have a predictable system,
> with nothing but noise or routine variation. Therefore, we
> shouldn't overreact or declare that we see trends that
> might not be valid. Use the three rules to find signals.

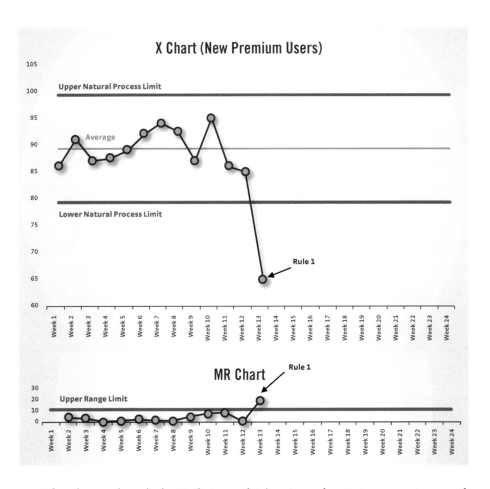

After this week with the ***Rule 1*** signal, it's a time when it *is* appropriate to ask, "What happened last week? Do we understand why we had only 65 new premium user registrations? What can we learn from this, and how can we restore performance to its usual levels?"

This data point could be an outlier that's caused by a problem that's easily resolved. For example, it could have been that the company's website was down for a day or that there was some other technical issue that could be solved and, hopefully, prevented through root cause analysis and other systemic improvements. It's necessary to resolve that problem, but, as Deming said, putting out a fire does not improve the quality of your house.

It's also possible that this data point below the Lower Limit is the start of a shift in performance, which would be even more troubling. If there wasn't a server outage, we might worry that our service has suddenly become less popular. Has a new competitor entered the market? Will we expect performance to now fluctuate around a new, lower average? Do we have a new system, or can we restore things to the old expected level of performance? The PBC answers those questions, but "there's no substitute for knowledge" (as Deming would say) about our company and the broader system in which we operate.

> "There's no substitute for knowledge." W. Edwards Deming.

If we had been tracking this metric on a daily basis, we might have seen a signal that we could have reacted to more promptly. In a scenario where some server interface was not working (and it was unknown for some reason), the company could have reacted after seeing a signal for a day instead of waiting for a weekly data point.

If we, indeed, restored the previous system, we'd expect to see our next data point in the metric falling within our previous limits. We see another signal in the MR Chart, which corresponds with a larger-than-expected change from point to point. This is nothing to be alarmed about since we know the system was restored back to its previous level of performance.

> Process Behavior Charts can help us find emergent
> signals, or we can use PBCs to test a hypothesis to see
> if the system has really changed significantly or not.

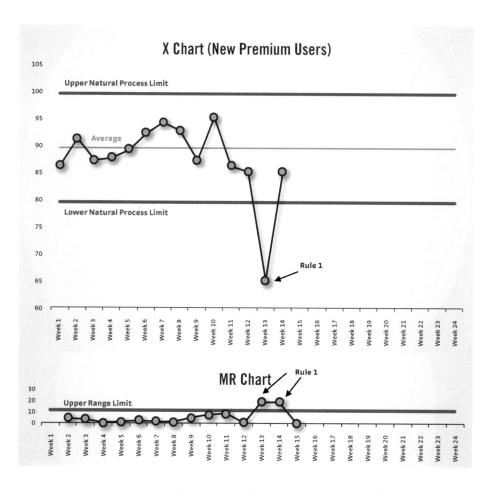

As we're monitoring performance and running the business (with less distraction caused by the reactive nature of our old red/green analysis approach), the PBC can be useful in helping us see any emergent signal. Or, we can use the PBC to test a hypothesis about a way we are trying to improve the system.

Let's say, immediately after the signal (or special cause) was resolved in Week 13, somebody had an idea for improving the system. Maybe they made a change to the server code that increased the performance of our software, making free-trial users happier (increasing retention rates) and attracting additional new premium users.

Our use of the PBC will help us make sure we don't declare victory too soon after one or two data points (unless we see a single data point that's higher than the Upper Limit).

Let's say the data continues to play out over the next few months:

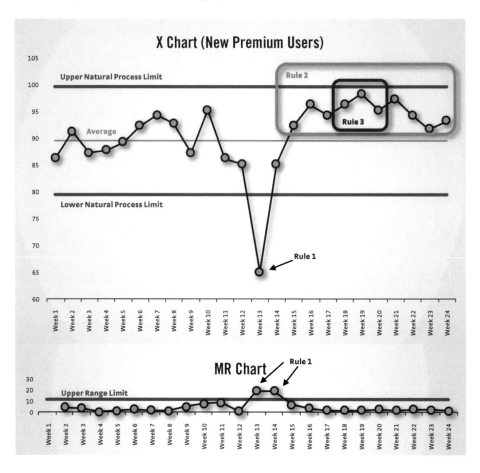

Over time, we would first see three consecutive points that are closer to the Upper Limit than the average (a ***Rule 3*** signal). This is our first sign of an upward shift in performance. A few weeks later, we'd see the eighth consecutive point above our old average. This is a ***Rule 2*** signal, which should make us feel pretty confident that we have a sustained shift in performance, something that reflects a new system. The PBC tells us something has changed. Hopefully, we're correct in our cause-and-effect assertion that the server-speed change led to this increase in new premium user registrations.

Again, saving the details of the calculations for Appendix A, we can illustrate the shift in performance by calculating a new average along with new Natural Process Limits, as seen below. The slightly lower Average Moving Range results in slightly narrower Natural Process Limits for the X Chart.

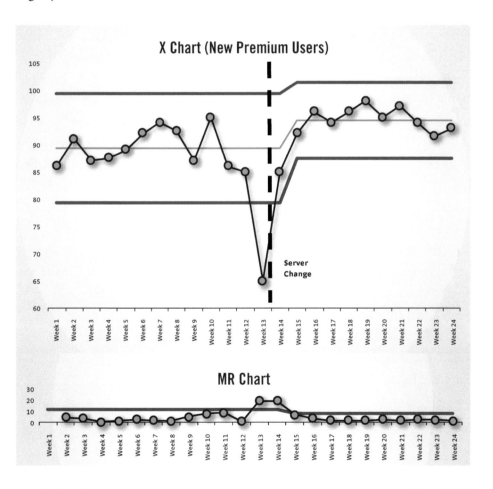

Going forward, we'd now expect this system to generate between 88 and 101 new user registrations each week, based on the new Lower and Upper Limits. This is a new predictable system that's likely to exceed that previous target of 90 most every week. Since the new average is about 94, the metric would only exceed a possible higher target of 95 only a little under half the time, unless the team comes up with ways to improve the system.

The CEO shouldn't react to or ask for an explanation for every below-average data point or every data point that's below the target. The CEO and her team should look for signals that expose a change to the system, either positive or negative. Additionally, they should continue developing, testing, and evaluating systemic changes that are intended to improve performance — using the PBC to test the hypothesis about change to see if performance has improved significantly or not.

If we want to increase our average from 90 to something higher over time, doing so requires more systematic analysis than asking "What went well last week?" Leaders and the team can try to identify factors that might lead to more premium user registrations. The team can test a hypothesis that says, for example, "If we create more compelling blog and social media content, more people will find our site, leading to more premium users." This hypothesis can be tested and evaluated using the PBC over time. If we see a signal, it tells us the system and its results have indeed been changed.

In a situation like this, we should also be careful not to ask people to increase this metric "at all costs" in a way that's dysfunctional, suboptimizing, or harmful to the company as a whole (for example, dramatically lowering the price of the premium registration in a way that would hurt profitability).

Less Wasted Time Means More Improvement

Thinking back to Ries's question of:

"If we stopped wasting people's time, what would they do with it?"

He provides a good answer in *The Lean Startup*:

"We would achieve speed by bypassing the excess work that does not lead to learning."[25]

We would do so by bypassing "excess work" that includes leaders asking for explanations for every up and down in a metric. Writing fiction only consumes time and creates stress — it doesn't lead to learning. If learning leads to improvement, we can improve more if we overreact less.

Thinking back to the Bowling Chart from Chapter 1, the bottom three metrics had a lot of red:

Team Engagement	Necessary Information Available Survey	UP	Actual	67.3%	50.8%	48.3%	70.4%	46.9%	40.6%	61.3%	70.5%	50.9%
			Target	80.0%	80.0%	80.0%	80.0%	80.0%	80.0%	80.0%	80.0%	80.0%
Patient Experience	Likelihood to recommend	UP	Actual	76.4%	78.4%	80.5%	70.0%	46.0%	40.0%	60.0%	70.0%	50.0%
			Target	79.9%	79.9%	79.9%	79.9%	79.9%	79.9%	79.9%	79.9%	79.9%
Patient Experience	Hospital rating	UP	Actual	76.4%	77.7%	77.6%	77.6%	77.2%	77.6%	77.0%	75.0%	63.0%
			Target	77.5%	77.5%	77.5%	77.5%	77.5%	77.5%	77.5%	77.5%	77.5%

Are all three of those last red data points worth reacting to? Do they all require equal attention? No. If the leader told people to go investigate to find an explanation or a root cause, three sets of effort are required. The Bowling Chart cannot filter out noise or show us signals. If every red number is a priority, then nothing is. The PBC methodology can help.

Below are the X Charts for each of those three metrics. What do we see?

The first two charts show predictable systems, with results that are just fluctuating around an average. The red color coding means that the system is not capable of meeting the target consistently, as we would like. The way to improve these first two metrics won't be found in reactive "What happened?" questions. We need to study and improve the system, as we'll discuss in Chapter 4.

The third chart, however, does show a **_Rule 1_** signal in that last month. All three metrics are red. The third metric also tells us that something has changed in the system. Performance is not just fluctuating — it has gotten worse. In this case, we must ask, "What has changed?" If we are equally consumed by investigating the first two metrics, we might not have enough time and capacity left to investigate the signal. That's why we need to use PBCs to focus our attention and efforts instead of reacting equally to every red data point.

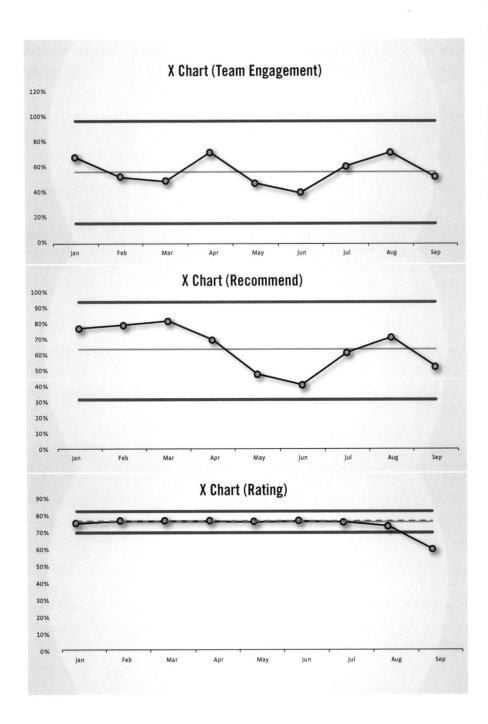

Case Example From a Software Company

Since 2011, I have worked with a startup software company called KaiNexus and its CEO and co-founder, Gregory Jacobson, MD. As I've coached Greg and participated in various company meetings, one of the standard metrics that gets reviewed in weekly marketing meetings is the number of "Tier 1 leads." This is not a vanity metric since attracting more leads that are qualified as potential customers means that, at the end of the sales pipeline, the company will have more customers, increased revenue, and long-term financial success.

Each month, Maggie Millard, the company's director of marketing, would mention the latest number and how it had changed from the previous month. I would often remind the team that two data points is not a trend or not to simply compare each number to a goal.

Maggie started looking at a Run Chart and would occasionally show it in the meeting. Even with a chart in front of them, she would still continue the old habit of saying things like, "I'm very concerned about the number of leads this month. It's low. I don't want it to be low."

Greg and Maggie wanted to say this number was increasing, so it might have been tempting, as many organizations do, to add a linear trend line (in red) to the Run Chart:

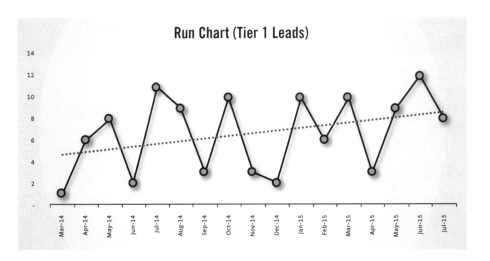

The dotted line added to the X Chart "paints a picture," but it's misleading. Why is it misleading? The linear trend line implies the number will continue to increase up and to the right forever. In this case, the PBC, as we will see below, tells us the data is fluctuating around the average.

In a meeting, Greg would sometimes ask, "Why were leads down last month?" Maggie would respond, "Let me look into it."

Maggie estimates that she might spend an hour digging into her marketing software, trying to identify causes of a decrease. Were there fewer leads because website traffic was lower? Was the conversion rate lower? Did we have less website traffic because our last webinar wasn't as well attended as before? Was the search ranking for key terms worse that month?

She did her best to come up with a reasonable answer, but it was an example of writing fiction. The honest answer for a given month might very well be, "I don't know." They'd review the number the next month, and it would often be higher. She might not have a solid answer for why it increased, either.

The KaiNexus team was asking questions that incorrectly implied there was a special cause for what might have been data points within the range of routine variation.

Using a Process Behavior Chart

After seeing the Run Chart go up and down over time, I suggested that Greg and Maggie use the Process Behavior Chart methodology. They were open to my suggestion since they knew some KaiNexus customers used this method with their own metrics.

I took the Run Chart and used its 16 data points to calculate the baseline average and limits. The average was 6.65 Tier 1 leads, and the Upper Limit was calculated to be about 20. The calculated Lower Limit was negative, so that limit becomes zero since we can't have a negative number of leads.

The initial X Chart looked like this (and the MR Chart, not shown, had no signals):

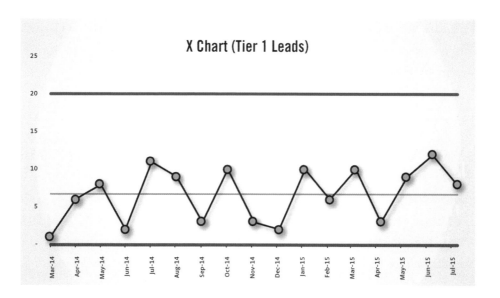

Note: The exact numbers have been changed, but all of the data is proportional to reality.

What did we see? About half of the data points in the X Chart were above the average, and about half were below. There are no signals. It was a predictable system in that timeframe.

While Greg and Maggie wanted to say this number was increasing, the statistical reality was that the number of Tier 1 leads was fluctuating around an average. The bad news was that it wasn't increasing. The good news, in a way, is that we could predict that the number of Tier 1 leads would be between zero and 20 each month if nothing changed in our system.

"But I don't like those limits," Maggie said when I showed her the chart. As I explained, a key point about this method is that it's the voice of the process speaking to us, even if it's saying something different than we might like to hear.

Again, in a predictable system, asking "What happened last month?" is unlikely to provide great insight. But, we can work to improve the system as to increase the average number of Tier 1 leads. This requires a more systematic form of problem solving and analysis, as we will explore in Chapter 4.

Working to improve the system would be more difficult than playing games with the data. Instead of cherry picking two data points to claim "the number of Tier 1 leads increased from two in December 2014 to 12 in June 2015," Maggie thought about different ways to increase the number of Tier 1 leads.

> This is the voice of the process speaking to us, even if it's saying something different than we might like to hear.

When Maggie stopped looking for root causes for noise, she was able to spend that time more productively, including writing more blog posts and additional eBooks that would attract more website visitors that would convert into more leads. She formed a hypothesis that could be tested and evaluated using our PBC over time.

As the months went by, we started to see, through the X Chart, that the number of Tier 1 leads was no longer fluctuating around the average:

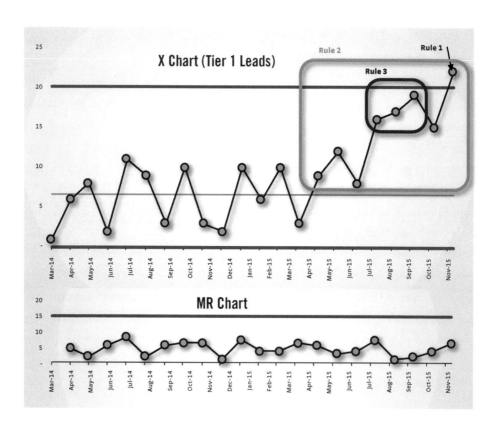

We saw multiple signals. The last data point was above the Upper Limit (*Rule 1*). And, we see three consecutive points that are close to the Upper Limit (*Rule 3*). And then we confirmed eight consecutive data points above the average (*Rule 2*).

The PBC shows that the system had improved. The earliest we could have felt very confident about that was September 2015, when we had that third consecutive point near the Upper Limit (*Rule 3*).

The number of leads had clearly increased. Maggie could make a compelling case that her attempts to change the system made a difference in the performance of the metric. In fact, one use of PBCs is to help evaluate an attempted improvement.

Our next question was, "Is the number of leads now fluctuating around a higher average?" Or do we now truly have an "up and to the right" situation, where the number of leads is increasing but still fluctuating around a growth trend line?

Over time, we saw that the metric continued to increase, as shown with additional data points added to the PBC, below:

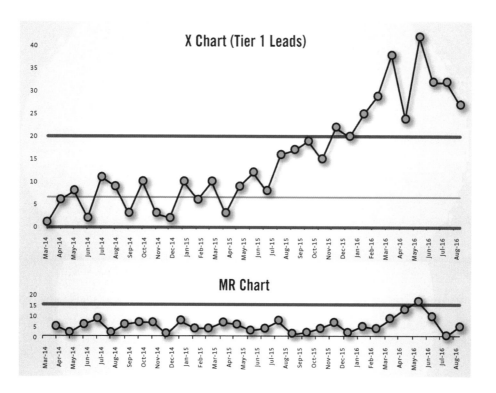

We calculated a new average and limits starting in September 2015, when **Rule 3** was triggered.

The PBC with the shift looks like the chart, below:

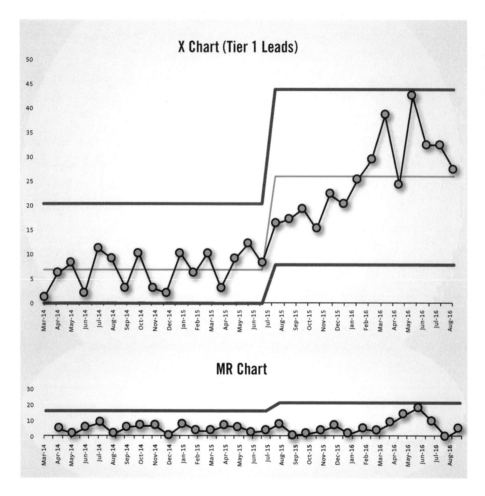

The PBC tells us that we have a new predictable system, in which the number of leads is now fluctuating around an average of 25.6 instead of 6.7. The Lower and Upper Limits tells us we can predict that the number of leads will now fall between 8 and 43 in future months unless we make further changes to the system that generates leads. It's possible that we'd see signals as time goes on that indicate that the system has changed again.

One other way to look at the data, with a slightly more complex X Chart, where the metric started fluctuating around a linearly increasing average, at least for the time, as shown below. In this form of X Chart, we have a central line that's an increasing diagonal line instead of a horizontal average. The Lower and Upper Limits have the same upward slope in parallel to the increasing average. In a growth-trajectory chart like this, the same three rules apply when looking for signals.

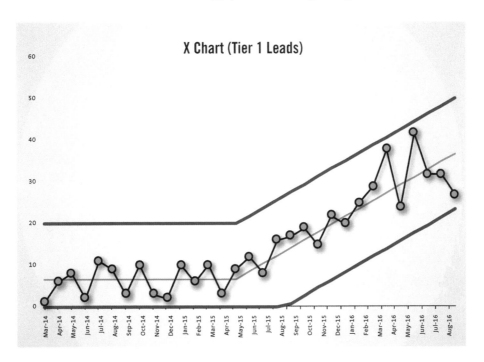

There are no signals. Drawn this way, we arguably have one predictable system that existed from March 2014 to May 2015. Then, the system changed and became a system that predictably increased (fluctuating around that increase instead of fluctuating around a predictable average).

The number of leads might keep increasing, or it might level out at a new horizontal average, as could be starting to happen in the last few months of the above chart. If the performance was starting to flatten out, we'd see proof of that through one or more of the three rules for finding signals, as shown below in a hypothetical scenario.

In this case, we'd first detect a **Rule 3** signal, then a **Rule 2**, and then a **Rule 1** signal. This chart depicts three different systems: a flat fluctuating period, a linear growth period, and then another flattening out. Signals on the upper side of the growth average and limits would be positive signals that would suggest the number of leads would be approaching exponential growth.

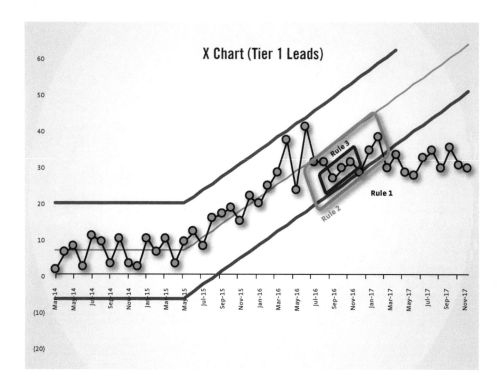

The main point of the story is that Maggie and Greg had learned how to stop overreacting to every data point. One day, Maggie asked, "So I shouldn't lose sleep over last month's number being down a bit if it's inside the limits?" No, she shouldn't.

Learning to use Process Behavior Charts within KaiNexus has freed up time, reallocating time spent writing fiction to, instead, improving the systems and processes that create better performance.

The Power of More Timely Measures

The default in many organizations is to measure and display metrics on a monthly basis. The downside of monthly metrics is that we have slow cycles of learning and slower detection of signals in our metric. The slow detection of signals might mean we have "underreaction" metrics, where we're not improving as quickly as we could.

> KEY POINT #8: More timely data is better
> for improvement. Daily is better than weekly,
> which is better than monthly, as long as we
> don't overreact to every data point.

Using weekly or even daily metrics can help us see signals or prove process shifts more quickly. But, we need to remember not to overreact to the variation in the more frequently tallied metric.

Next, we see an X Chart created with monthly data (the hidden MR Chart showed no signals):

> Learning to use Process Behavior Charts within
> KaiNexus has freed up time, reallocating time spent
> writing fiction to, instead, improving the systems
> and processes that create better performance.

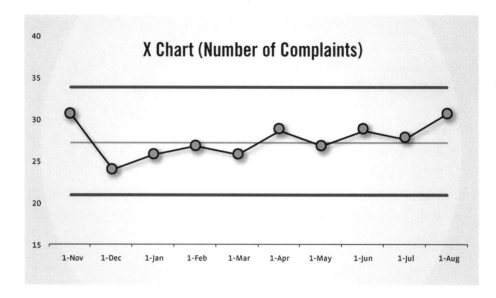

It's a predictable system that fluctuates around an average of about 27.5. If we plot the same underlying data as a weekly X Chart, it looks like this:

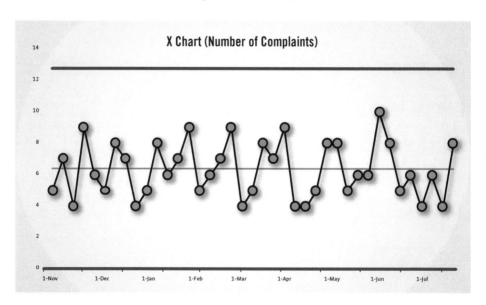

The weekly average is about 20% of the monthly average, which isn't surprising. What might be less intuitive is the higher level of variation in the week-to-week data points. The routine variation always gets smoothed out when presented in monthly buckets. Proportionally, the limits are narrower for the monthly metric.

Faster Detection of Shifts

If there is a shift in the performance of the system, the weekly chart will show us the signal more quickly than a monthly chart. Let's say the number for the entire month of August is 55, as shown in the X Chart, below.

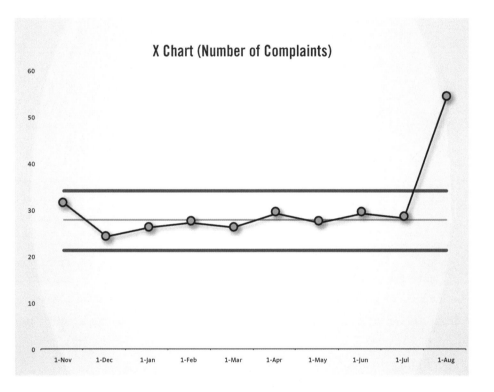

We'd find that *Rule 1* signal at the end of August if it is a monthly metric. That's a relatively slow response,

As visualized above, it's not a predictable system. We don't know yet if the August data point is an anomaly or the beginning of an upward shift.

How could we find a signal more quickly? If the metric is something that can be counted, like customer complaints, one way would be to react as soon as the cumulative count during the month is higher than the Upper Limit. Or, we could track this as a weekly metric, as shown below:

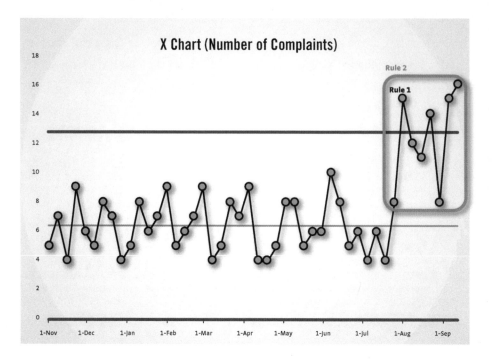

The weekly chart says so much more to us, and more quickly. We can detect the ***Rule 1*** signal after just one week instead of waiting until the end of August. Additional weekly data points help us see that it appears to be an upward shift in the metric, with a ***Rule 2*** signal. It appears that the first data point above the Upper Limit is the start of a new system.

What has changed? Can we understand why the number of complaints has increased? Can we find countermeasures that get the number of complaints back down (if not to a lower number than before)? In Chapter 4, we'll discuss ways to do that.

Not Hiding a Short-Term Blip

One other thing to consider with monthly charts is that, since they smooth out some of the week-to-week variation, there is some risk that a monthly chart would hide a single week's signal.

In another scenario, let's say the weekly data looks like the following, where the August 1 weekly data point was just a one-time blip instead of being the start of a shift in performance:

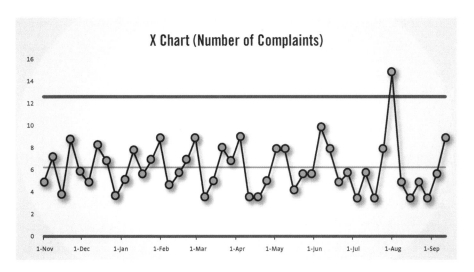

The monthly X Chart for that same data would not show a signal:

We don't know yet if any Rule 1 signal is an
anomaly or the beginning of a shift. Only more
data points can provide more clarity.

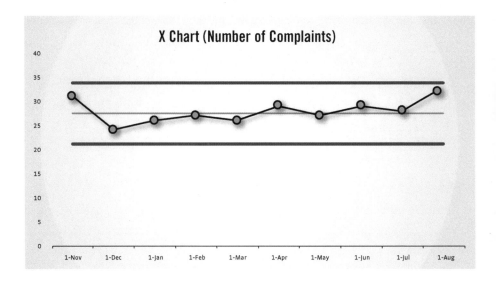

We'd lose a chance to learn and prevent future blips had we used a monthly chart.

Again, a weekly chart tells us more than a monthly chart. A daily chart might be even better. On the one hand, when a Bowling Chart or Run Chart is generated on a weekly, daily, or even hourly basis, there's a risk that more data points create more opportunities for the inappropriate reaction to noise, which leads to more wasted time spent looking for special causes that don't exist. On the other hand, the PBC mindset and an improved understanding of variation in a system, of course, keeps us from making those mistakes.

Summary of Key Points Introduced So Far:

KEY POINT #1: We don't manage the metric; we manage the system that leads to the results, and we lead the people who help us improve the system.

KEY POINT #2: Two data points are not a trend.

KEY POINT #3: "No data have meaning apart from their context."

KEY POINT #4:   A chart will always tell us more than a list of numbers.

KEY POINT #5:   The job of management is not just to look backward but also to look forward and predict, if possible, what is likely to occur.

KEY POINT #6:   There is variation in every metric or data set. Process Behavior Charts filter out noise so we can identify signals.

KEY POINT #7:   Don't waste time explaining noise in a metric. There is no simple, single "root cause" for noise.

KEY POINT #8:   More timely data is better for improvement. Daily is better than weekly, which is better than monthly, as long as we don't overreact to every data point.

CHAPTER 4

Linking Charts to Improvement

The main objective of the Process Behavior Chart methodology is not to post technically correct charts on a bulletin board (or in an electronic "dashboard"). The aim is improvement. PBCs help by pointing us toward the systematic improvement approaches that are most appropriate for a given situation. There's a time to be quick and reactive (when we see signals), and there's a time to step back and more calmly analyze and improve a predictable system.

By now, we know not to react to noise in a predictable system. However, a system or a metric being predictable doesn't mean that performance is acceptable. We have two dimensions in our analysis:

- Is the metric predictable?
- Is the metric meeting our target or goal?

This chapter explores a methodology as outlined below:

- If we have an unpredictable system, then we work to eliminate the causes of signals, with the aim of creating a predictable system.
- If we have a predictable system that is not always capable of meeting the target, then we work to improve the system in a systematic way, aiming to create a new a system whose results now fluctuate around a better average.
- When the range of predictable performance is always better than the target, then there's less of a *need* for improvement. We could, however, *choose* to change the target and then continue improving in a systematic way.

Improving an Unpredictable System

I often see organizations using Run Charts with red and green zones shaded in to represent their targets. The organizations would waste less time reacting to noise if they added PBC thinking to their approach.

Below, we see an unpredictable system that is a special case, where the calculated Upper Natural Process Limit is coincidentally about the same as the chosen target.

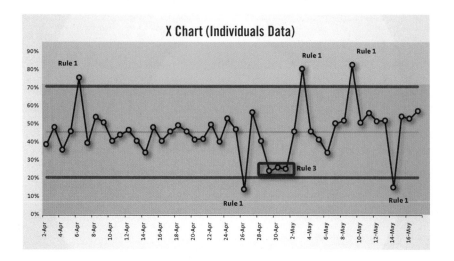

With an unpredictable system that's mostly (or completely) in the red, it's important to first identify and eliminate the causes of exceptional variation — to make the unpredictable system predictable. Once we stabilize the system, it's easier to then focus on systematically improving the stable system and boosting its average performance (and, perhaps, reducing variation).

Some signals in the negative direction (downward, in this case) indicate a problem needs to be solved. In some cases, we might have records of server crashes, production downtime, power outages, or other unusual situations that create a temporary *Rule 1* signal. When we see a *Rule 1* signal followed by an immediate return to the range of routine variation, it could be a sign that the cause was identified and solved, at least for the short term. The proverbial fire was put out. Or, the cause was an external problem or factor that went away on its own.

We should ask if the same fires are starting over and over. If so, can we learn how to get better at learning from each fire with the objective of preventing them in the future?

In the cases, above, where we had a *Rule 1* signal up into the green, we might have lost an opportunity to sustain an improvement. Why did we suddenly exceed our Upper Limit and then fall back to the old range of performance? Again, we shouldn't have reacted because it was green; the reason to react is the point being outside of our limits (or any other signal).

The PBC methodology tells us that any exceptional variation is the result of a change that's significant enough to overwhelm the many causes of routine variation that previously existed. It's worth the time and effort to look for a root cause — what has changed or what is different? Whether the signal is positive or negative, it's easier to identify the cause of a recent signal, which is why we continue updating and evaluating PBCs over time.

When we are working with an unpredictable system, we should investigate and identify the root cause of each signal, as we will discuss in the next section. This is true even if we have a chart that's more often (or always) in the green zone, or better than our target, as shown below.

Over time, as the system is made predictable, we could see an X Chart like this:

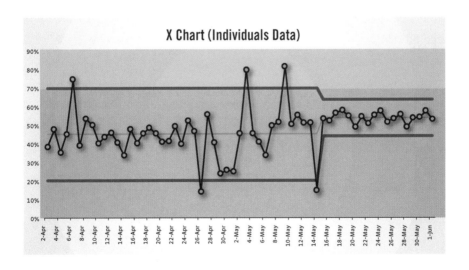

The average is higher, and the limits are more narrow. This system is still not yet capable of ever hitting our target, so the improvement must continue.

Identifying a Root Cause of a Signal

One method for identifying a root cause that was made popular by Toyota and the Lean Manufacturing movement is sometimes called "the five whys." Toyota's website quotes the late Taiichi Ohno, one of the creators of the Toyota Production System, as advising people to "Ask 'why' five times about every matter."[26] We might extend that quote to say we should ask "why" five times about "every matter that is a signal of exceptional variation in the system."

In a predictable system, with nothing but routine variation, there is no single root cause for any change in performance. The point-to-point variation in a predictable system's PBC is caused by the interconnection of dozens, if not hundreds, of variables that always exist. We should search for a root cause only when we see a signal in a metric.

The "five whys" method can also be used in healthcare or any setting where we have processes and systems.[27] Eric Ries and the Lean Startup movement have popularized "the five whys" method for a new audience outside of manufacturing.[28]

When we see a signal, we can start by asking, "Why did that occur?" Ohno recommended that we "go and see," rather than brainstorming in isolation in a conference room. In more recent years, Toyota's then-chairman Fuijo Cho recommended we "Go see, ask why, show respect."

Some classic examples of "the five whys" are shown with a simple, linear line of questions. The real world is often more complicated, where we might have multiple answers to each "why?". But, the classic example, shared by Toyota on its website, shows five sequential "why?" questions that continue to drill deeper into the causes, instead of asking five random "whys."

The Toyota example is:

"Why did the robot stop?"

The circuit has overloaded, causing a fuse to blow.

"Why is the circuit overloaded?"

There was insufficient lubrication on the bearings, so they locked up.

"Why was there insufficient lubrication on the bearings?"

The oil pump on the robot is not circulating sufficient oil.

"Why is the pump not circulating sufficient oil?"

The pump intake is clogged with metal shavings.

"Why is the intake clogged with metal shavings?"

Because there is no filter on the pump.[29]

In the Toyota example, for some reason they don't continue asking, "Why was there no filter on the pump?" In their example, the apparent countermeasure would be to replace the filter on the pump. That might alleviate the problem in the short term by keeping the robot from stopping. But, what if the filter had been removed by a worker because it was needed on another robot?

We could continue asking why:

Why is there no filter on the pump?

Because a team member removed it.

Why did the team member remove it?

They needed it to fix a different robot, and the stockroom had no filters available.

Why were there no filters in the stockroom?

Because the reorder point inventory level was set too low.

So, is the inventory system the root cause of the problem? We could go even further and ask, "Why was there a problem with the inventory system?" and so on.

We don't always ask "why?" exactly five times in every situation. I've taken to calling this approach "the many whys."

The point is to keep asking "why?" until we find a countermeasure that not only fixes the problem in the short term (some call this "containment") but also does something to prevent the problem from recurring over the long term. There's as much art as there is science in root cause problem solving, with elements of trial and error to go along with discussion and data analysis.

The thought process here can be described as a "Plan, Do, Check, Act" (PDCA) or "Plan, Do, Study, Adjust" (PDSA) cycle. This is often an iterative process with a number of cycles.

We "Plan," which includes defining the problem and understanding the current state, including root cause analysis. The "Do" phase is an opportunity to test a change and then "Study" the effect to see if we got the predicted results and if there were any unintended consequences. We might "Adjust" or go through another PDSA cycle if our first attempt at a solution didn't work.

At some point, we might suspect we have identified the root cause of a signal. When we are talking about or brainstorming possible root causes, that's initially only a hypothesis about a root cause. We don't yet *know* that we have found the root cause if we're just talking.

I've been taught by former Toyota leaders that you have to test your root cause hypothesis. If you implement a countermeasure that's meant to address the root cause, you need to look to see if performance improves. If we react to a negative **Rule 1** signal of a single point outside our Natural Process Limit, we'd look to see if our countermeasure puts the metric back into its prior range. If not, we probably haven't found the root cause (or we didn't find an effective countermeasure), so we adjust and "spin the PDSA cycle" again, as they say in many Japanese organizations.

If your countermeasure puts the process back into its normal, predictable range, you can turn off the countermeasure to see if the poor performance returns. It might not be ethical to do so in some situations, for example, if we are trying to solve a patient safety problem.

Improving a Wine Bar: A Signal in the Noise

A few years back, my wife and I considered buying a wine bar. As part of our due diligence, the owner of the business provided financial data, including monthly revenue numbers.

I created PBCs for some of these key business metrics to see if they were predictable. Many people might look at revenue as a monthly average or a run rate. But, I thought it was important to understand how much routine variation existed and what the Natural Process Limits on revenue might be.

Looking at the X Chart for revenue, we don't see any signals. It appears that the wine bar system, as a predictable system, could be expected to produce anywhere between the Natural Process Limits of $27,615 and $49,588 each month, with average revenue of $38,601.

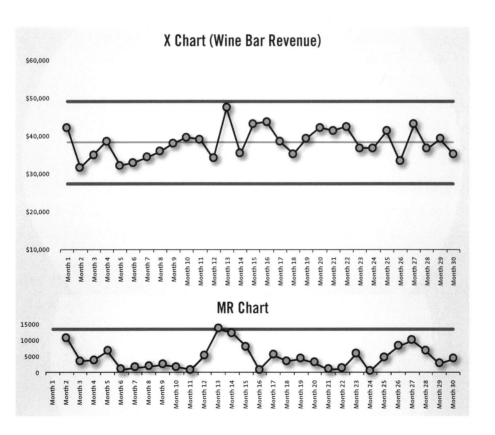

Note that this chart had no target. I was merely looking at the voice of process to see if business performance was predictable and how much it varied. If we had bought the business, we would have set targets — but we would have worked together to reach them rather than just putting pressure on people.

Looking at the MR Chart, there is a **Rule 1** signal in Month 13, where the MR value is slightly above the Upper Range Limit. This is a case where the MR Chart detects a signal that is not visible by using the X Chart alone.

I asked the owner if he knew why revenue had fluctuated more in Months 12, 13, and 14 (going up more than usual and then going back down immediately). He didn't know. The manager couldn't point to anything, and it didn't appear to be due to seasonality.

The PBC tells us that, most likely, something was different in that time frame. It's hard to have a good recollection looking back 18 months, which is one reason why it's important to use PBCs for real-time management, not just as a retrospective-analysis tool.

We decided, for a number of reasons, not to purchase the business. Had we bought the bar, I would have taught the manager how to use PBCs to look at some key monthly, weekly, and daily metrics. I would have reinforced the importance of not reacting to or explaining every up and down in the metrics. We wouldn't have wasted time on root cause analysis when no signals were present.

Improving a Predictable System

Had we bought the business, my wife and I would have worked with the manager to focus on improving the system in ways that would have boosted average revenue and, perhaps, reduced some of the variation in different ways.

Many of these ideas might have been called "Just Do Its," where we simply test an idea and evaluate using the PDSA cycle. We could have asked the manager and employees for ideas. They might have suspected that some wines served by the glass were underpriced compared to what the local market would pay. One of them might have suggested ways of bringing in more customers on slow nights, like offering wine education or wine trivia nights. These would have been simple to test and evaluate without overcomplicating our analysis or the improvement process.

We could have also asked loyal customers for ideas. One might have suggested expanding the "wine of the month" retail club to include food-product pairing. As customers of the wine bar, we had often wished that they offered more than cold snacks and appetizers. Even with limited kitchen space, it might have been possible to offer some hot-food options, which might have allowed customers to, essentially, stay for dinner instead of having wine and then going home or to a restaurant.

We could have also tried to talk to people in the community who were *not* customers to see if there was something about the bar that was unappealing. There were probably a number of marketing and promotional ideas that could have increased traffic and revenue to the bar.

If we came up with dozens of ideas about how to increase revenue in a profitable way, testing one idea at a time might be the surest way to prove a cause-and-effect relationship between a change and our metrics. We could start implementing an idea and then look for signals of a significant change to the system.

The fastest (and strongest) signal would be implementing a change and then seeing a *Rule 1* signal (in this case, revenue above $49,588 in a month). Confirming the positive effect of a change would take at least a month if we're using a monthly metric (and longer to find *Rule 2* or *Rule 3* signals that show a shift in results). Looking at a weekly metric would give us faster signals, as was discussed in Chapter 3 (and our PBC methodology would prevent us from overreacting to any week's results).

People often ask if it's better to test one idea at a time, since trying many changes at once might make it difficult to determine a cause-and-effect relationship between changes and results. In some circumstances, that slow-and-steady approach might maximize our learning about the system, but improvement might go slowly. Does "slow and steady win the race" in all situations? Probably not.

If a business is in a solid position without any severe threats to its existence, we might have the luxury of prioritizing possible changes to try one at a time. We might use a tool like a "PICK chart" to identify and start with changes that have a relatively low effort and a relatively high expected impact. Ideas can be sorted and grouped on the PICK chart, as shown below, recognizing that the categorization and prioritization might be a subjective prediction.

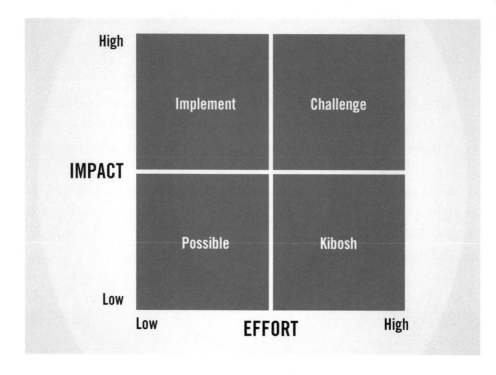

Ideas in the upper left part of the "Implement" quadrant would be tested first. Those in the lower right might indeed be "Kiboshed," although, we can work to turn a single high-effort idea into a number of smaller, lower-effort ideas.

If the survival of the business is at stake, or if the level of patient harm is at unconscionable levels in a hospital, the necessary (or moral) thing might be to try many ideas at once. We might get more improvement on our important metrics more quickly and might accept the tradeoff of learning less about cause-and-effect relationships in our system.

The Bad Case: Predictable and Always Red

In an underperforming system, we might start with a metric that is wholly incapable of producing any results that are better than the target.

An example of an X Chart and a target is shown below:

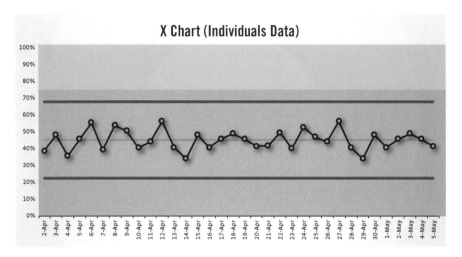

Even though all of the data points are worse than the goal, we have a predictable system. That's the good news. On the other hand, our main concern is the bad news that there's no chance of ever being in the green unless we can improve the system significantly.

No amount of cajoling, incentives, or motivational speeches will help. We might more likely see distortions of the system or the numbers if too much pressure is placed on people to show better results without also having a method for improvement.

Our focus should be on boosting the average performance of the system. If the average increases to be the same as the target, we'll have a system that's better than the target roughly half of the time. We'd want to keep improving until the entire range of the Limits is better than the goal. In the last chart, above, we'd want the Lower Natural Process Limit to be higher than the target.

How do we improve a predictable system? Again, we don't do so by asking "Why?" or "What happened?" about just any data point. We have to think systemically. Improving a system requires, well, systematic approaches to improvement.

A Systematic Problem-Solving Method

Just as Toyota provides one method for root cause analysis, "the five whys," the company and the Lean methodology also provide a broader systematic method that we can use to analyze and improve a predictable system. This method is either called "Toyota Business Practice" (TBP) in the company or "A3 Problem Solving," more broadly.[30]

You might prefer Six Sigma or other problem-solving methodologies. What matters is having an approach that's effective in understanding and improving the performance of systems in a way that's sustainable and never ending.

The Toyota Business Practice (TBP) approach has eight steps, which can also be mapped to the Plan-Do-Study-Adjust (PDSA) cycle concept:[31]

1. Clarify the problem (P)
2. Break down the problem (P)
3. Set a target (P)
4. Analyze the root cause (P)
5. Develop countermeasures (P)
6. See countermeasures through (D)
7. Monitor both results and process (S)
8. Standardize successful processes (A)

And, an implied ninth step is to adjust when changes don't lead to better results or outcomes. This might mean going back to the first step, if necessary.

You might have noticed that five of the eight steps are in the "Plan" phase. That's no accident, as this approach tries to guard against the human tendency to jump to solutions. We also tend to assume that our ideas are good, thinking about "implementing" instead of "testing." If we tested "Just Do It" ideas, as discussed earlier, and found that they didn't improve the system, that should prompt us to then try this more rigorous TBP approach.

When we have an unpredictable system or find a signal, the reactive problem-solving process should be a faster, more urgent PDSA cycle. We could even think of the earlier reactive examples as a faster cycle through these eight steps.

The steps of TBP are often written out on a single sheet of A3-sized paper (which is approximately 11" x 17" paper in American size), hence the alternative names like "A3 thinking." More important than the exact format or labels on an A3 problem-solving template is the thought process and mindset.

As Wheeler said about Process Behavior Charts, TBP and A3 problem solving are, essentially, a way of thinking with some tools attached.

Faster, Better Heart Attack Care

Let's look at a hospital that has set a target of 45 minutes for what's informally called "door to balloon" (or "D2B") time for patients who arrive at the emergency department with a suspected heart attack.

There are different types of heart attacks, with one of them being called ST-Elevation Myocardial Infarction (STEMI). If it's determined, through specific tests, that a patient is having a STEMI, it's very important for the patient to be sent to the cardiac catheterization lab to have a blockage cleared by a "balloon" that's inserted into the patient's heart and expanded.

D2B is typically defined as the time that elapses between the patient's arrival to the hospital until the point in time when the balloon expansion is started. If each patient's measured D2B time is charted on an X Chart, we might see that the average and the Lower Limit are above the hospital's target (noting that, of course, lower is better for this situation):

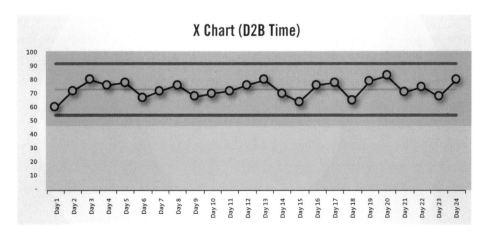

One cause of routine variation in the metric could be measurement error. For example, the measure could be imperfect for a patient if the exact time of arrival isn't recorded because they had to wait a minute after coming through the door, or if the cardiac cath lab estimated the time because, well, they were busy trying to save a patient's life. Improvements that make these measures more accurate might reduce the point-to-point variation, which would have the effect of narrowing the Natural Process Limits without necessarily affecting the average.

National guidelines for good STEMI care include a door-to-balloon time of 90 minutes or less. The hospital has set a target of 45 minutes because they realize that leads to better patient outcomes. With an Upper Limit of 91.9, the good news is that this predictable process will nearly always get a patient's blockage cleared within 90 minutes. But, with a Lower Limit of 54.4, we see that this system is incapable of ever delivering on that 45-minute goal.

The PBC tells us that we have a consistent system that's generating different results. The chart shows us the range of routine variation for this system. If we try to ask, "What was different that time when it was only 60 minutes?" we might end up wasting a lot of time looking for an answer that's likely not there. It might not be a good use of time to say, "We'll investigate every above-average time!" The same system that delivers below-average times will also produce, to no surprise, above-average times.

To improve the system, the hospital might form a cross-functional team to study the existing work and care that's provided before jumping to brainstorm solutions. The team might map out the end-to-end process (or "value stream," as we'd call it in the Lean methodology) to look for steps that can be eliminated or rearranged. One hospital decided to change its process to ensure that the electro-cardiogram (ECG) was always done first. That systemic change might lead to a new, lower average (along with reduced Natural Process Limits).

The hospital might also create a cross-functional team to break down silos between the emergency, cardiology, and cath lab departments. In some cases, the teams have discovered that one cause of the delay is waiting for a cardiologist to read the ECG after waking them in the middle of the night. The team might work together to train the emergency physicians to read the ECG (and to do so accurately). Or, the main effort might involve getting the cardiologists comfortable with giving up that idea.

Asking people to work faster or try harder might not lead to sustainable results (or quality might suffer as a result of rushing or cutting corners). We need to improve the system so that it leads to improved results. Each change to the system might show a step-function improvement, leading to a chart that shows shifts in the average and limits:

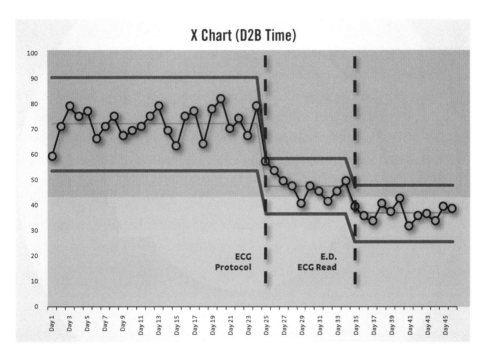

The initiation of the "ECG first" protocol created the second system, which has a new, lower average of 48.3. The signals of the shift include all three rules being triggered shortly after the process change was made. As we can see in the chart, this second system is capable of beating the 45-minute target only occasionally.

That middle range, with an average near the target, creates a situation where we would have to be very careful not to overreact to every individual red data point or every data point that's worse than average. We'd look for signals (and react to them) while continuing to apply systematic problem solving to the situation.

Having the ED physicians read the ECG creates yet another new system, where the Upper Limit is a bit higher than the target, meaning this system will quite consistently meet the hospital's target of 45 minutes (and, more importantly, the objective of better patient care). We'd expect this new system to predictably produce door-to-balloon times between 26.1 and 48.9 minutes unless we made additional improvements.

We'd also monitor the PBC to look for negative signals, such as eight consecutive times above the newly established average of 37.5 minutes. If we saw any data point greater than 49 minutes, it would be appropriate to investigate and to look for a root cause of that exceptional variation. We would want to know if the new process was no longer being followed in some way or if some other new problem had occurred.

In this example, we used the X Chart to confirm two tests of change. We would also look for any positive signals that suggest that the system has changed in a positive direction. For example, if we saw three consecutive times between 26 and 32 minutes (*Rule 3*), we'd want to go talk to the people working in the system to see if they've made any changes to the system. Or, we might find out if there are external factors causing the lower time and a potential shift in the system.

Remember, the PBC filters out virtually all of the noise, allowing us to find the signals if they exist. It doesn't tell us what the cause of the signal is — we have to go find that through our knowledge or by learning about the system.

The Best Case: Predictable and Always Green

Some organizations use Run Charts (instead of Process Behavior Charts) where, instead of just drawing a target line, they use green shading in the background to indicate parts of the chart that are better than the target and red shading to indicate which section of the chart is worse than the target. It's a visualization of the "green is good, red is bad" binary mindset that we're working to move beyond with PBCs.

Let's say that color coding is combined with a PBC that adds an average and Natural Process Limits to the chart.

The best situation is one where the PBC predicts that we are always going to be in the green zone of a chart — unless something changes in the system.

We might see a chart like this:

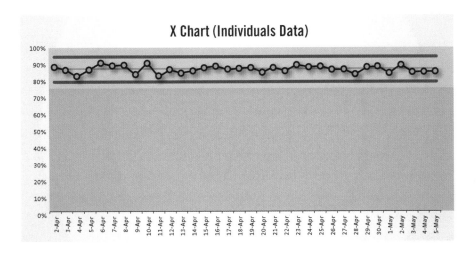

We have a predictable process, as we don't see any data point outside of the limits, we don't have runs of eight or points above or below the average, and we don't have a cluster of three points near the limit.

Since up is better for this metric, we have a situation where the Lower Limit is higher than our target line. We can be confident that this metric will remain green.

Of course, we can still try to improve the system. But, we likely won't be able to improve by asking why any particular high data point (lower than the Upper Limit) occurred. There's nothing to learn about any single high data point since it's generated by the same system that produces the below-average data points or the lowest ones that we can see (that are higher than the Lower Limit). Everything we see here is routine variation.

Why Continue Improving an Always-Green System?

Just because we are always green doesn't mean we can't improve. Now, if this is one out of six metrics we are tracking, and others are sometimes (or always) in the red, we might prioritize our improvement efforts elsewhere.

If all of our metrics are always green, we can still choose to improve. Remember that targets are often quite arbitrary. Some targets could be the "voice of the customer," and they might say we don't need to perform better, especially if they are the type of organization that would react only to a single red data point, which is most likely an overreaction.

However, even if we are meeting the customer requirements, we can still work to improve a system for a number of reasons. If the above chart represents a metric like "first pass yield" (the percentage of time when quality is good without requiring rework or rejection of some work), we might still choose to improve beyond customer requirements because higher first pass yield means fewer defects, which would likely reduce our cost and improve profitability.

In the case of the previous PBC, we need to avoid the old tendency to be happy as long as the number is in the green zone. It's possible to have a single data point that's below the Lower Limit, a *Rule 1* signal, while still being green. If we were using a Bowling Chart, the green color coding for that data point would mean we missed a signal. This signal, or any other of our signal types, means that the system has degraded, which merits investigation.

A single data point between the Lower Limit and the goal could be an indication of future red data points to come and if it's the start of a downward shift in our metric that will establish a new, lower average. In this case, we would want to start investigating and problem solving before the metric hits the red. It's also possible that the single data point is due to a fluke occurrence or a short-term problem that's easily identified and solved. Either way, a missed signal is a missed opportunity to improve by preventing future events of that type.

A similar thought process would apply for *Rule 2* or *Rule 3* signals, as we would probably want to understand a downward shift in the process even if results are still green. Letting the average drop without learning why might lead to future drops that eventually take us into the red. A problem like this is easier to solve when the problem (the drop in the average) is smaller, so it's best addressed sooner than later.

Again, we want to avoid reacting to every single below-average data point (or even a short run of fewer than eight below-average points). We need to prioritize our problem-solving time by not overreacting to noise in our metric.

Reacting to Signals in a Predictable System

Once we have a predictable metric, we hope to keep it that way. Below, we see an example of a metric that has been predictably better than the target. That is, until the last data point:

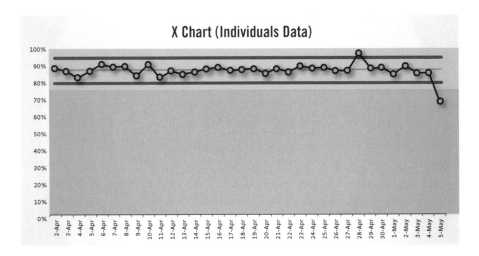

In an organization that is still using the red/green analysis method, there might not be any reaction because that last data point is still green. Why should we be concerned about signals that are still better than the target? The signal means the system is no longer predictable. It could be a warning that we're about to see a sustained negative shift in performance.

When we also see a signal that's still in the green, we can react and find countermeasures that are intended to restabilize the system, which helps us be more assured of future performance. We shouldn't wait until it gets into the red to react. Organizations that react only to red will miss this opportunity to take action when there's still a chance of preventing further decline into the red.

In the chart above, we first see a ***Rule 1*** signal above the Upper Limit that represents a missed opportunity for learning. If there was a temporary change or some other factor that boosted performance that day, we should understand the cause so we can try to lock in that better performance going forward. If we could shift the performance of this metric further into the green, it gives us even more margin of error against the system degrading into the red. And, we never know when a customer (or a manager) might increase our target.

The Website's Gotten Slow

Let's look at the case of a website's loading time, where a faster time (a lower number of seconds) is better. You might see a predictable system that suddenly shows a ***Rule 1*** signal, as shown in this X Chart:

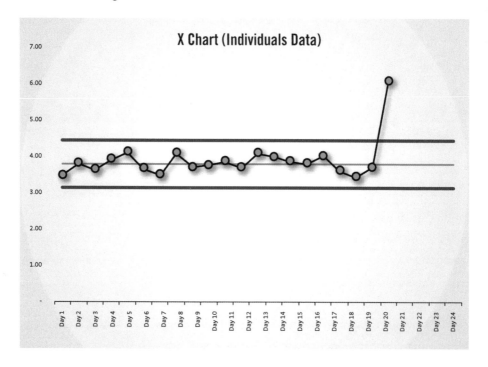

We might react by calling our web hosting company to see if there is a known problem. If they say, "No, we're not having server or connectivity problems," we might then look to see what changed in our site.

Let's say we installed a Wordpress "plugin," let's call it Plugin A. If we think the problem is Plugin A, we can disable that plugin and re-run the site speed test. If there's no change, we know that the cause wasn't Plugin A. We planned, we did, we studied, and now we'll adjust.

We discover that Plugin B was recently updated to a new version. If we turn off Plugin B and the site-loading speed goes back down to the usual faster range (within the limits), we might feel confident that we've found the root cause. Then, we'd turn the countermeasure off (by turning Plugin B back on) to see if the problem returns. If we see a pattern like the chart below, we could feel confident that we'd identified an actionable root cause of the problem and that our countermeasure works. We might not know why Plugin B slowed down the site, but we might be happy that the problem seems to have gone away.

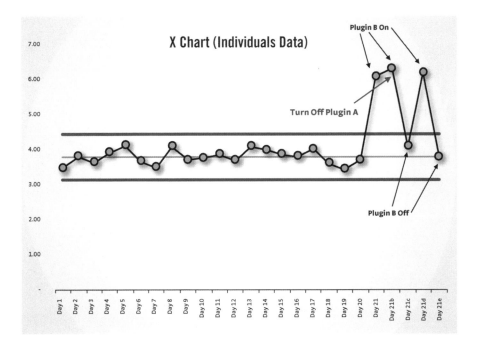

Again, the PBC shows us that turning off Plugin A had no effect but turning Plugin B off and on did prove a cause-and-effect relationship that helped us improve.

As we've seen in this chapter, there's a time to react and there's a time to step back and be more systematic in our approach to improving a system and its results. By practicing the PBC methodology, we can learn to react to statistical signals instead of reacting to:

- Every up and down
- Every point that's worse than the goal
- Every point that's worse than average
- Any other arbitrary goals or rules that might be used

The PBC gives us a better way.

CHAPTER 5

Learning From
"The Red Bead Game"

There are many ways to learn about variation, predictable systems, management, and improvement. We can read books (thank you for doing so), watch videos, and go to classes. Arguably, the most effective model for adult learning includes experiences and simulations.

One of the classic exercises for getting a gentle, but impactful, introduction to the concepts and methods in this book is the "Red Bead Experiment," sometimes called the "Red Bead Game"(games do sound more fun and less threatening than experiments, I suppose). The Red Bead Game was used by W. Edwards Deming over the last decade of his life and career. It was created by Bill Boller, of Hewlett Packard, as a gift for Dr. Deming in 1982.

Deming used the game in his famed four-day seminars, which I first heard about from my father, who attended one in the late 1980s. The game is also detailed in the book *Four Days with Dr. Deming*.

Deming started his seminars by asking, "Why are we here?" His answer was, "To learn... and to have fun." Adults learn more when we're having fun.

I've facilitated my adaptation of the Red Bead Game many times over the past 20 years. There are many scripts and explanations available online and you can even find a video of Deming facilitating the game on YouTube. There are some core elements of the game that are usually consistent, but you can add your own wrinkles to it without changing some of the core lessons or takeaways.

Dr. Deming would say, at the start of the game, "Here is a stupid experiment... one you'll never forget."

In Chapter 3, we saw the scenario where the manager reacted to every figure, every uptick or downturn (this happens quite often in most modern workplaces). When we overcompensate and ask people to spend time explaining each data point, we consume time and energy that would be better spent improving the system. Managers who react to every data point are well intended; it's not their fault they haven't been exposed to a better way.

Looking for "Willing Workers"

In facilitating the game, I play the role of an executive — it could be a plant manager, a division president — who oversees the fictional company called "Beads as a Service" or BaaS. BaaS is a fast-growing company that sells a monthly subscription service that ships a carefully curated box of beautiful beads to customers each month.

This month's offering is a box of white beads, and we need to hire more employees to ramp up production. The first job that's posted is for six frontline workers who will "produce" beads in our process. Deming always referred to these participants as "willing workers" to emphasize the idea that, ultimately, people choose to come to work and that, generally, people want to do quality work in which they can take pride.

I display job requirements that say workers "must be willing to put forth best efforts." The participants who volunteer as willing workers get told that continuation of their job is dependent on performance. After all, BaaS has a "pay for performance" culture, which "is only fair," as I tell them, play-acting the role of a traditional manager. But not to worry, the workers will receive training after hiring is done.

Two inspectors are hired with the expectation that they can "distinguish between red and white" and that it's preferable that they can count to 20. An inspector general is hired, a role requiring "a loud voice," in addition to the requirements of the inspectors. Finally, a recorder is selected to collect and record defect data from our process.

We have 10 employees who all want to do their best. New hires are told that BaaS hires only the best of the best and expects that all employees are above average. This usually triggers some chuckles and worried expressions on people's faces. Everybody wonders how they are going to perform and if they're being set up to succeed.

Now, it's time to produce beads. The tools of the trade are a plastic container that's full of small beads — most of them are white, but there appear to be some red beads mixed in. The willing workers are told that the red beads are left over from last month's bead-box shipments to customers. There's also a paddle with fifty holes that is used to gather or produce the beads, as shown in the figure, below:

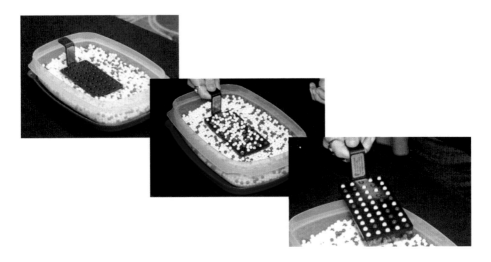

The willing workers are given training, in which they are given a very detailed job-instruction document that explains how to dip the paddle into the container. As the facilitator, I demonstrate how the work is done, dipping the paddle into the beads, giving it some gentle agitation, as spelled out in the document, making sure all of the paddle's holes are filled, and withdrawing the paddle.

A ridiculous level of job-instruction detail is given, including directions to tilt the paddle at precisely 47 degrees to let excess beads fall off. "Let gravity do the work," the willing workers are told. It's a "highly engineered" approach and "proven best practice," the workers are told, as if to give them confidence in the job ahead.

As I demonstrate the bead-production process, there are inevitably some red beads on the paddle. The red beads are defects, I tell the willing workers, reminding them that this month's BaaS box selection is white beads. Any red beads on the paddle will have to be sorted out by the shipping department. Defects only increase our cost, and there's a risk that red beads might slip through to customers. We can't have that. "Defects are unacceptable! You do care about quality, right?" I declare.

If any of the willing workers starts to ask a question, they're quickly shut down. There's no time to waste. No need for discussion. We need to get to work! Sadly, this isn't a culture of continuous improvement.

The willing workers are to produce their 50 beads and then hand the paddle to the first inspector, who then counts the number of red-bead defects and calls out that number. The first inspector hands the paddle to the second inspector, who is told to do their independent count (since it's important to have accurate data about our defects, I explain). The paddle is then handed to the chief inspector, who does a final count and says the number loudly, so the recorder can write the number on the flip chart quality record.

The willing workers are reminded that quality is, ahem, a reflection of their skill and diligence. Some of the willing workers quickly catch on to the joke, but others seem nervous. They realize that the bead-production process is a random number generator. They can hope for luck. They can only hope to be treated fairly.

Producing Beads (and Defects)

The willing workers are told to start their first round of production (the flip chart suggests there will be four or five rounds). The first willing worker, Lorenzo, steps up and dips his paddle into the container.

Inevitably, somebody will ask if they can pick and choose individual beads. "No, that will take too long, so that's why you need to use the paddle," I'll tell them. "Just dip the paddle in... time is wasting."

Lorenzo pulls the paddle out, and the inspectors agree there are six red beads. "Six!" calls out the chief inspector, and the number is recorded. Next up, Michael has just four red beads on his paddle. "Great job!" I tell him, and I add, "This is an encouraging trend! More white beads, fewer red beads — you can do it!"

Next up, Gugu cringes as she pulls the paddle out of the container. "Too much red," she says with a sigh. "Fifteen red beads!" says the chief inspector. I shake my head and ask Gugu if she paid attention during the training. I ask the group what color we're supposed to ship this month and they reply, "White beads!" And what color are defects? "Red!" I remind them, "Remember, your future job security is based on your performance."

The next willing worker, Ferkut, draws 14 red beads. More head shaking. As the manager, I tell them, "Look at this variation! That's unacceptable! We're all using the same process, the same equipment, the same raw materials, so how could there be variation?"

Walter draws nine red beads. I say, "Why can't the rest of you be like Michael and Lorenzo? Look at their performance! They show what's possible!" The last willing worker, Kyösti, comes up to the bead box, perhaps against his better judgment, and draws 10 red beads. The round is over.

Time for Management to "Help"

As leader of this production team, it's now time for me to lead a quick meeting to discuss our performance. Unfortunately, this meeting is mostly one-way communication. In a high-performing organization, we'd see huddles, where the leader invites input from the team about process improvement. No such opportunity is given here.

Michael is called forward and is presented a Willing Worker of the Day certificate. "The rest of you should watch how Michael does his job. He's the epitome of excellence and dedication to quality!" The other participants, again, realize that "performance" here is essentially random. The "worker of the day" recipient realizes they are benefiting from chance. That doesn't help create much joy and pride in their work.

We see a summary of Round 1 results below:

	1	2	3	4
Lorenzo	6			
Michael	4	☆		
Gugu	15	Willing		
Ferkut	14	Worker of		
Walter	9	the Day		
Kyösti	10			
TOTAL	58			

The red-bead system delivers the results that it's designed to achieve. It also delivers variation. These statements are true in any system.

Even though the proportion of red beads in the container is the same for each willing worker, they get different results from person to person and from round to round. The willing workers aren't told this yet, but 20% of the beads in the container are red. We'd expect that, on average, 10 of the 50 beads drawn each time would be red. People rarely get exactly 10 beads on their paddle, though.

Because I've ignored or stifled any attempts that the willing workers make to speak up, such as asking, "Can we remove the red beads from..." I yell, "NO! Do not question the procedures. Don't insult the engineers like that!"

Gugu is brought up in front of the group. I chide her and the group, saying, "We are a performance-based culture here at BaaS, but we are fair. You're going to be placed on probation and given a warning. Be more mindful of quality and, if you improve, you'll be able to keep your job. Otherwise, we'll find another willing worker. We're going to hold you accountable." Somebody usually chuckles knowingly at this last phrase, recognizing it from their own workplace.

Gugu slumps her shoulders and walks away. Usually, people are in on the joke here, but I have had people get very competitive and very upset for being scolded in the midst of the admittedly silly exercise. They seem to forget sometimes that BaaS is a fake company.

Producing More Beads

As the second round of production starts, a few things inevitably happen. Lorenzo, up first again, draws 15 red beads after getting just six the first time. "How have you gone from one of our best producers to one of the worst?" I ask. "Have you been hanging out with Gugu after work?"

Michael, our "Willing Worker of the Day" award winner, draws 12 red beds. "Clearly your certificate has gone to your head!" I exclaim. This seems to reinforce the idea that praising people causes them to slack off, when, in reality, they are regressing to the average.

Gugu draws 11 red beads. "Well, at least you're improving. I'm glad that the progressive disciplinary process has gotten you focused, Gugu. Keep up the good work. I like this trend, and I can see you'll be at zero defects before long."

As their leader, I call "time out" and stop production. "It looks like things are headed in the wrong direction here with quality. So, management has decided to make a significant investment in your future. We were at a leadership conference where another organization raved about the quality posters they had recently purchased. Quality improved quite a bit after they bought them! We want those same results, so we've also purchased some posters that have just arrived. Don't say that management doesn't invest in quality!"

The posters are revealed. The willing workers are not impressed.

As the rest of the willing workers complete the round, Walter is praised for his dedication for drawing just two red beads. "See, those posters really make a difference!" The posters make a difference until they do not — when Kyösti draws 16. It's time for another huddle. The Round 2 results are shown below:

	1	2	3	4
Lorenzo	6	15		
Michael	4	12		
Gugu	15	11		
Ferkut	14	10		
Walter	9	2		
Kyösti	10	16		
TOTAL	58	66		

Again, Leadership Tries to Help

I lecture the group, saying, "We still have too much variation! Our total number of defects has gotten worse, going from 58 to 66. Don't you care about quality? Don't force management to close this plant because of bad quality. It's adding a lot of unnecessary cost for the shipping department to sort out the red beads before the boxes go out. That's a lot of rework. We need to do better!"

At this point, everybody in the huddle is just staring at their shoes, waiting for it to be over.

"Again, management is very concerned about quality. We need to do better. We've been reflecting, and we realize we've failed you. We neglected to give you a target! Targets are motivating. We've been too vague about the need to avoid red beads. We now have a more specific target... the target is three! And here is a poster to remind you of this."

"And since we're a pay-for-performance company, we're also going to offer an incentive. This crisp $20 bill will be the reward for anyone who can limit their red beads to three or fewer. We think this will be very motivating. You do like money, right? You do like your jobs and your continued paycheck, right?"

Walter speaks up and asks, "Hey, do I get the incentive payment? I only had two red beads last time!"

He's told, "No, that would be unfair to the others. You've proven it's possible to hit this target... just do it again, and you can get that bonus payment every single day!" It's very rare for somebody to get three or fewer red beads. I expect my $20 is safe.

As the third round progresses, some unsurprising things happen. After his previous scolding, Lorenzo draws 11 red beads, an improvement from his previous 15.

I continue saying silly things, such as, "Remember to work smarter, not harder! Tip that paddle at precisely 47 degrees... let gravity do the work... follow the procedure... Be Lean... quality is up to you!"

Michael's performance improves a bit to nine (again, inadvertently reinforcing the idea that yelling at workers about quality somehow leads to improvement). However, he's still doing worse than his initial award-winning performance. Management stopped giving out the "Willing Worker of the Day" certificates since they seem to increase the number of defects.

Gugu's positive trend ended with two data points, as her defects went up from 11 to 12. Management again steps in to introduce an "exciting new program... we call it the STAR program. Now, this program was very expensive, so we are sure it is going to work. We want you all to be STARs." Here's what they have to do before they produce beads:

- Stop!
- Think
- Act
- Review

Of course, we have a poster. The willing workers are starting to get burned out on new programs. Some of them get frustrated that management is not doing anything to improve the system that is designed to generate a high number of defects. They're starting to feel abused instead of supported. "Management would like to remind you that they have every ability to shut down this plant if quality doesn't improve," I tell them.

Believe it or not, "STAR" is a real program that some organizations use in their attempts at improving quality or becoming a "high-reliability organization."[32] Lecturing people to stop and think about their work in a badly designed system is not a path to quality.

Walter must have been focusing too much on the incentive program, or maybe the STAR program distracted him because his defects went from two to twelve.

We review the results, shown below, and see that the target and the incentive program had no effect. Again, the team usually realizes that it wasn't going to work — or if it did, it would be due to chance. And that's no way to run a business.

	1	2	3	4
Lorenzo	6	15	11	
Michael	4	12	9	
Gugu	15	11	12	
Ferkut	14	10	6	
Walter	9	2	12	
Kyösti	10	16	16	
TOTAL	58	66	66	

The willing workers are chastised for not improving. There's still too much variation. Some red beads are slipping through to customer, and they're canceling their bead-box subscriptions. I tell them, "Management has decided it would be unfair to punish everybody by closing the factory. Since we're a performance-driven company, we're forced to lay off our bottom three performers. I hope you feel bad for letting down your co-workers and your management team."

The totals for the first three rounds are:

- Lorenzo   32
- Michael   25
- Gugu   38
- Ferkut   30
- Walter   23
- Kyösti   42

Kyösti, Gugu, and Lorenzo are called forward. With a somber expression, I shake their hands and thank them for their service.

The remaining three workers are told, "Yeah... we've been left a little short-handed. We're going to have to ask you, our top performers, to pull double duty in this next day. Don't worry, we'll let you rest in between your two rounds of bead production."

One Last Gasp

In our fourth round, with each worker pulling a "double shift," we see similar variation from person to person. We see a now-predictable range of seven to 16 red beads being pulled. The total is 65, not much better than the previous two rounds. People look dejected. In spite of their "best efforts," we see no improvement, as shown on the flip chart, below:

	1	2	3	4
Lorenzo	6	15	11	X
Michael	4	12	9	9/13
Gugu	15	11	12	X
Ferkut	14	10	6	7/16
Walter	9	2	12	10/10
Kyösti	10	16	16	X
TOTAL	58	66	66	65

After the totals are tallied, I tell the remaining willing workers, "I hate to have to tell you this, but we've heard from corporate headquarters that we've run out of time. The factory is being shut down. Please collect your things... and, please, don't take any beads home with you as a souvenir. Thank you for your service."

And so ends the exercise, with people ready to tell me what an ineffective manager I have been. I hope they remember that I was role playing.

Lessons Learned

When I start the debrief discussion, one of the first questions usually asked by participants is, "Why didn't you let us improve the system?" As the facilitator, I often ask in a tongue-in-cheek way, "Why didn't you speak up more?" It was my responsibility as a leader to create an environment in which it was safe and worthwhile for people to speak up. Instead, I shut down their attempts to speak up or question things.

Effective leaders don't blame people for not speaking up or for giving up in their attempts to improve since that's almost always the predictable result of a bad culture, where people get beaten down and worn out. They're often reduced to just showing up for a paycheck.

It's always interesting to see how seriously most willing workers take this, even though they realize it's just a silly exercise. People are competitive. They want to do quality work. This reminds me of several Deming quotes:

> **"Workers will try to do a good job even when they know they cannot."**

And

> **"Management cannot motivate people; they can only hope to stop demotivating them."**

The exercise illustrates how it's unfair to ask employees to perform better than the system's design and management will allow. "A bad system will defeat good people every time" is a phrase often attributed to Dr. Deming. What was this red-bead system capable of producing? The number of red beads fluctuated in a way that seems random — because it was.

Darril Wilburn, a former Toyota manager, has said, "It's the responsibility of leadership to provide a system in which people can be successful." Toyota leaders have long given credit to Deming for his role in teaching Toyota about quality, improvement, and leadership.

What Does the PBC and the Voice of the Process Tell Us?

When the game is done, the participants are right to be frustrated; the management and improvement methods we tried during the game didn't work. They're also correct that it can be difficult to answer these questions without a good method for doing so. Keep in mind we start the workshop with this game, so they generally haven't been exposed to the PBC method that can help answer these questions, as we'll see below.

As with any metric that's displayed as a table of numbers, it's difficult to see any trends in the results that we posted on the flip chart. In the workshop, the first

PBC that everyone sees is for the number of red beads. We use the 24 data points as our baseline for calculating the average and the limits and see a chart like this:

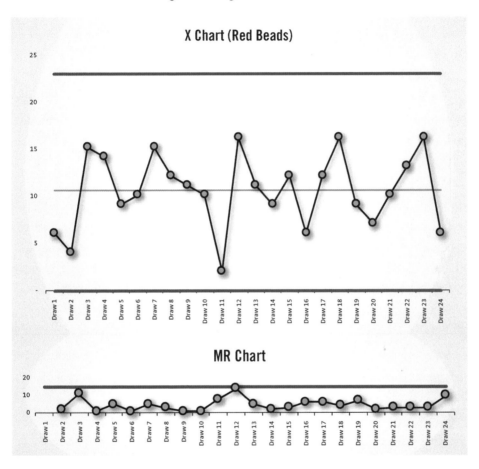

Using the method described in Appendix A, we calculate the average to be 10.46. The Lower and Upper Limits calculations give us -1.8 and 22.7, respectively. Since we can't draw a negative number of red beads, zero becomes the effective Lower Limit.

It can surprise participants that the average is never exactly 10, which shows that short-term averages can vary from the long-term expected average.

Participants often point out that the red beads aren't likely to be perfectly evenly distributed in the box, either.

What does the PBC show us? Red-bead production is a predictable system. We'd expect that, if we kept playing, we'd get between zero and 22 red beads in any given draw. Any single result in that range is due to randomness or the routine variation in the system. Every single data point is noise.

Dr. Deming would have said we can't ask people to perform better than the limits of our PBC. Setting a target of three means that somebody is eventually going to be rewarded for a random result, which, again, is no way to manage a business.

An Occasional False Signal

In one recent workshop where I facilitated the experiment, we *did* have a single data point that was just above the Upper Limit that was calculated for that session (the X Chart limits are not always the same each time you facilitate this). Having a **Rule 1** signal (or any signal) is an unusual occurrence in the Red Bead Game, as I think I've only seen that happen one time out of dozens of games.

Was there a root cause of what appeared to be a signal in that case? I can't think of anything. The system was the same for the one draw that generated the data point that was above the Upper Limit. I didn't see the willing worker distorting the system by intentionally picking up and hand-placing red beads onto the paddle or anything like that.

That rare occurrence illustrates how we can, once in a while, get a false signal in an X Chart. This is due to the probabilistic way in which the limits are calculated, which tries to balance out the risk of false signals and the risk of missing the signal of an actual change to the system.

In real life, it's possible that we have a data point outside of the limits, even when nothing has changed. A system with a false **Rule 1** signal will fix itself, in a way, as the metric will then return to the predictable range within the limits — because the system hasn't changed.

On the other side of this balance, there might be a situation where there was indeed a change in the system, and we see, for example, a single data point just barely above the Lower Limit or a tiny bit below the Upper Limit. If there is a missed signal, that situation will also likely correct itself when we see a **Rule 1** signal (a future data point outside of the limits). If it was an actual signal of a shift, we'll see **Rule 2** (eight consecutive points on the same side of the average) or **Rule 3** (three out of four points closer to the limit than the average) signals once more evidence of a system shift becomes apparent through additional data points.

Even with this small amount of uncertainty about false signals or missed signals, using these rules is more effective than guessing what data points are signals. And using PBCs is certainly more helpful than Bowling Charts.

What Did Management Try to Do?

All of the management tactics used in the exercise focus on the willing workers trying harder or being more careful. These are generally ineffective or unsustainable strategies in any workplace.

The willing workers can't do anything to improve their performance, short of cheating in some way. Inevitably, somebody produces a large number of red beads and intentionally drops the beads back in, hoping to have better luck the next time. When this happens, I start complaining about their poor productivity (again role-playing as an unhelpful leader).

When the BaaS manager makes a big production out of walking away and turning their eyes from the bead-production area, that inevitably leads to a willing worker knocking red beads off the paddle with their finger in their attempt to get fewer red beads. I would call that predictable human behavior in a bad system. This sort of cheating is especially likely to happen when the system includes rewards, threats, or punishment.

With the red beads, willing workers can be pressured to do two of the things Joiner said could happen in a system: they distort the system (flicking red beads off of their paddle), or they distort the numbers (intentionally reporting or writing down a false number). They're not given the ability to do the more-constructive third thing: improving the system.

As Deming said:

> **"The worker is not the problem. The system is the problem. If you want to improve performance, you must work on the system."**

In many real-life scenarios, employees and lower-level managers don't get support and collaboration for improving the system. Employees who started their career or job with pride in quality and high ethical standards are often forced to turn to what some describe as unethical behavior. We could call it trying to keep their jobs.

Think of the various American school districts where teachers or principals have been pressured into helping students cheat on standardized tests. Or, where teachers who had parties where they erased and changed answers after the fact, all in the name of boosting scores and performance evaluations. A "worker" in Deming's quote could include principals or even district superintendents who are powerless against broader societal problems that could negatively affect test scores that they're pressured to improve.

Or, think of the hospitals in the National Health Service in England, where clinicians, staff, and managers were given a strict target that patients should not wait in the Accident & Emergency Department for more than four hours. So, some patients were kept waiting out in the ambulance to keep the clock from starting. In other cases, patients were admitted unnecessarily just before the four-hour mark was reached. The implied threat of punishment for a long A&E stay was apparently worse than the cost or consequences of an unnecessary admission.

How Can BaaS Improve?

How could the fictional BaaS company work to improve the system? Leadership needs to lead the way. As Deming taught, senior leaders are responsible for the system. Leaders need to help create a culture of improvement, which includes engaging everybody in identifying opportunities for improvement and working together with them to improve systems (instead of just dumping responsibility on the willing workers).

For one, the team could agree to stop returning red beads to the bin for the next round. This would lead to a downward trend in the number of red beads each round and, if we played long enough, we'd eventually have nothing but white beads remaining.

The long-term X Chart from one such experiment shows a series of **Rule 2** signals and downward shifts in the average and limits over time as we produced beads 200 times:

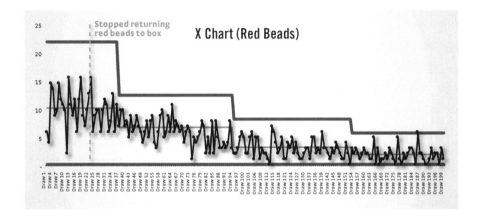

Starting with the 25th draw, we stopped returning red beads to the container. It took 113 draws to get a paddle with 50 white beads, and it started happening more frequently as more red beads were removed.

Willing workers often suggest that management could allow a one-time cleaning out of the red beads that are said to be left over from the previous month's BaaS shipment. They suggest that a little time spent up front would save a lot of time and hassle later on.

People suggest methods that could be tested in the real world, including weight-based filtering methods. The red beads in my kit are lighter than the white beads, by the way — yes, I checked. Another participant asked to check if one of the colors floated because he would then want to flood the kit to see if one color could be skimmed off the top.

It goes to show what creative people can do if leaders engage them in improving the system. Otherwise, their creativity goes into cheating and workarounds — or they just disengage.

In the Red Bead Game, leadership did not provide a system in which willing workers could hit the stated targets. In one running of the game, the lowest number of red beads in the first two rounds was six. One of the willing workers asked why I would set a target that was half that of the best performance to date. That seems unfair or unrealistic. Looking at the PBC, we see it is possible (while unlikely) that somebody gets three or fewer red beads (we saw it happen in the second round). The $20 incentive payment ends up being a lottery instead of a bonus that's based on individual performance or effort.

One lesson of the Red Bead Game is to stop blaming workers for performance that is designed into the system. A 1985 *New York Times* article quoted Dr. Deming as saying:

> **"People don't like to make mistakes. Change the system and the workers are suddenly a lot happier. They're no longer being blamed for what they have no control over."**[33]

Deming also said, "94% of the problems in business are systems driven and only 6% are people driven." The exact number, 90% or 93% or 94% (as sometimes attributed to or said by Deming over time), is what would have been called an unknowable figure.

The key point is that, in many organizations, management is more likely to blame the workers something like 94% of the time. The common mindset is, unfortunately, to blame the worker unless it's proven there is a system problem. In a culture of improvement, managers first assume the problem is caused by the system, unless it's proven that an individual took intentional actions that they knew would have led to negative results and that the worker wasn't forced into cutting corners or making a bad decision.

"Just Culture" is a framework that has gained popularity in healthcare in recent years.[34] Just Culture provides algorithms that are a useful way of determining if a problem is due to a system (meaning the individual shouldn't be punished) or if it's a situation where it would be fair and just to punish an individual for an intentional act. Not surprisingly, intentional acts and bad intents are rare in workplaces.

For example, one hospital repeatedly gave the wrong medication to multiple babies, leading to three deaths. Multiple nurses gave the wrong medication to the babies over multiple days, indicating that the pharmacy error (delivering a medication that wasn't supposed to be in the Neonatal Intensive Care Unit) was a systemic cause. The presumption that other nurses, if placed in the same situation, would have also likely made the same mistake was further evidence of a systemic problem.

Punishment would be "just" only in a situation with intentional acts that were expected to cause harm. It's, thankfully, a very rare case when a nurse murders a patient by giving them an intentional overdose. In those cases, punishment is just.

If BaaS were a Just Culture, management would realize that each worker was just as likely to have a bad outcome as the next. Nobody was intentionally trying to create red beads. Therefore, attempts to influence, reward, or punish individuals were just a waste of time. As mentioned in Chapter 1, Deming warned managers against the tactics used in the Red Bead Exercise, including "slogans, exhortations, and targets" since "the bulk of the causes of low quality and low productivity belong to the system and thus lie beyond the power of the workforce."

Can we learn these lessons and apply them to our own workplaces? Would we expect that hanging posters in an operating room or a software development team area is enough to reduce surgical errors and software bugs?

What Red Beads Exist in Our Work?

One challenging idea that comes from the Red Bead Game is that we might very well have, in effect, "red beads" in our own work. What are those "red beads"? Have we been overreacting to every small increase in the number of defects in our workplace? Have we tried some version of the things the facilitator does in the exercise, including punishment and rewards, incentives, arbitrary targets, posters, and slogans?

"Red beads" could be any defect that appears at varying degrees in spite of people doing the same work in the same system with the same level of effort, such as the number of:

- Software-development bugs
- Customer-support tickets or escalations
- Cars that need rework at the end of the line
- Customers or clients lost to the competition in a final selection round
- Patient falls or other incidents

When I've facilitated workshop debrief discussions after the Red Bead Game, I always ask, "What are the 'red beads' in your work?"

In one session, the Chief Medical Officer of a large medical center said:

"I think all of our patient safety measures are 'red beads.' Sometimes those numbers are higher and sometimes they are lower. I'm not sure what to do about it."

As the day progressed, the CMO learned to follow the methodology of this book. Instead of reacting to any single data point (or a perceived trend), he can use Process Behavior Charts to see if he is looking at the predictable results (routine variation) of a predictable system. If not, he can work to eliminate special causes until he does have a predictable system. He can monitor the PBC over time to look for signals, either positive or negative. He can also use systematic problem solving, as we discussed in Chapter 4, to improve the system to bring the average number of defects down as a series of step-function improvements toward zero. He learned a better way.

A Surgical Death Rate Simulation

If the Red Bead Game seems too whimsical for organizations facing issues as serious as medical error and patient harm, the BBC, of all places, has a fascinating simulator that was first published in 2010.[35]

In the simulation, you are a hospital that is going to be ranked and judged by the government based on your post-surgical death rates. Each patient at each hospital is given a random X% chance of dying (with the X being adjustable from 1 to 15%). This isn't realistic, but it makes each surgical outcome the equivalent of a "bead," if you will.

One round in the simulation has 100 hospitals each performing 100 of these surgeries, all having that same chance of death. The government sets an arbitrary target that says "death rates 60% worse than the norm are unacceptable." The implication is that hospitals with those higher death rates are doing something different, and wrong, and some sort of censure or punishment is due. In the simulation, your hospital is placed on an "unacceptable" list. In the real world, surgeons or leaders might get punished or even fired for remaining on such a list.

Here is the PBC for one session with the simulation, where each data point is the number of deaths for our hospital in a round:

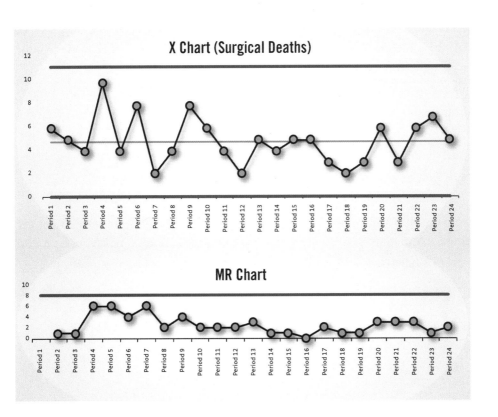

Not surprisingly, the PBC shows us we have a predictable system (the MR Chart also has no signals).

We can't predict that we'll always have five deaths. Every system and metric has a natural level of routine variation. This PBC tells us that we can predict that the number of deaths will be between zero and 12.

One lesson that comes from seeing a predictable system in a Process Behavior Chart is that we learn not to ask why there were 10 deaths in Period 4. Asking "What happened?" is, as we've learned, most likely a waste of time. The same system that produced 10 deaths also produced just one death in Period 5. Nothing changed. It's a perfectly random system. There are no "lessons learned" to be found from Period 5. Nothing changed.

But, in organizations, people chase non-existent root causes all the time. We should be asking "How can we improve the system?" instead of asking "What happened during that period?" when there are no "signals" in the chart.

A signal tells us that something has changed in the underlying system. We can use our three rules to look for signals. But, we see no signals here, which is not surprising, since nothing changed.

The government, in this simulation, has decided that eight deaths or more means your performance is unacceptable. Having eight or more deaths means that the hospital was unlucky in that period. Our predictable system is, sometimes, going to randomly produce death rates that are 60% worse than the average regardless of what the government targets and lists would call for.

Is that any basis for rewarding or punishing hospitals or surgeons?

Governments around the world do a lot of this — ranking and judging people based on differences that might be nothing more than randomness or noise in the system. There's not necessarily a difference in method, skill, or process. Judging people based on routine variation is unfair, and it's bound to be discouraging.

The Red Bead Game might be a "stupid" exercise, as Dr. Deming called it, but it's an experience that makes a large impression on those who participate.

CHAPTER 6

Looking Beyond the Headlines

By now, you know that two data points are not a trend, unless one of those data points is beyond our Lower or Upper Limits in our Process Behavior Chart.

In this chapter, we'll look at some case studies that start with a headline that makes an overly simplistic comparison of two data points. Comparing two data points can be misleading, and it can be harmful if an organization or the public draws incorrect conclusions. When we see two numbers or a simple percentage change being reported, even if a comparison sounds large, we should ask for more data, plot the dots, and respond appropriately.

Are Airline Pilots Staging a "Sickout?"

A few years back, pilots were upset with one of the major airlines. The airline was facing what was described as a high number of flight delays and cancellations. Again, a vague description like that doesn't tell us if we're looking at signal or noise in a metric like that.

The airline blamed the increased flight disruptions on a "surge of maintenance requests filed by crews" and an "uptick in pilots calling in sick." We don't have data to back up the terms "surge" or "uptick." We can't tell if that's signal or noise, especially without any data.

A news story said the airline had cancelled 310 flights that week, "more than the next three airlines combined."[36] The article also said that "for several days, more than half of" flights arrived late that week. That all implies those were unusually high numbers, but are there any signals? Did the airline have predictable metrics to begin with?

The airline accused pilots of conspiring to call in sick when they were healthy. The publicly available data showed the percentage of pilots who called in sick on the 18th of each month going back over the previous 12 months. It's unclear why they chose the 18th of each month as the basis for the measure; what is the context?

I'd be curious to plot every single day for a period of time to see if weekends are different and, if so, if that's part of the routine variation. Or, you could just plot weekdays. Another option would be to chart the weekly average of daily sickout rates as a way of taking that possible seasonality out of the equation.

The news story first compared the same date from one year to the next. The call-off rate was about 5% on September 18, 2011, and about 7.5% on September 18, 2012. What does that tell us? Well, one number is higher than the other. It could be a signal, or it could be noise. We can calculate that this year is 45.7% higher than the previous year. But is that evidence of a sickout or some other special cause? We need more than two data points to understand how much routine variation there is from day to day.

If we compared August 18, 2012 to the next month, the call-off rate increased from about 6.5% to about 7.5%. Was the number trending up over time? Did it increase suddenly? Again, we can't tell without more data.

The journalist added another comparison, writing, "[September 2012] is lower than the high point over the past 12 months, October 2011, and in the vicinity of sick leave in recent months." None of that text description tells us if we have a signal, even some number being the highest in the past year. That could still be nothing but noise.

Below is the PBC for this data. Keep in mind the alleged sickout occurred in September 2012.

> Comparing two data points can be misleading, and it can be harmful if an organization or the public draws incorrect conclusions.

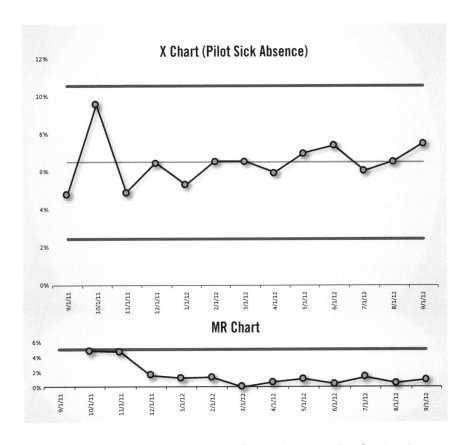

There are no signals in the X Chart (or in the MR Chart). There's zero evidence in the PBC that call-off rates are unusual in the month of September 2012 or that there's a sickout. It can't be proven from this data. The increase to 7.5% is part of the routine variation in this system. It's noise. There's no evidence that anything has changed. Even the high point of October 2011 is not a signal. There's likely no answer to the question of why sick-absence rates were higher that month.

Wheeler asks, in the context of PBCs, "Is it time to fix it?" The chart answers "no." If management and the union want to work together to reduce the average absence rate of 6.5%, they need to work together to improve the system.

Homicide Rates Have Dropped?

On a much more serious topic, a news headline read:

"San Antonio Homicide Rate Drops in 2017"

The article says, "2016 was one of San Antonio's most violent years with nearly 150 homicides. That number dropped in 2017 by about 16 percent to 125."

By now, you know to ask how much year-to-year variation is routine in that metric. When a metric changes, it's important to ask and answer the question of "Why?" — but only when we see a signal. If the metric is just exhibiting routine variation, any assertions about cause-and-effect relationships should be questioned.

As the news report says, "The drop is credited to a multi-agency task force created to tackle violent crime." It's possible that the task force led to a drop in the homicide rate — that's a signal. Or, if the metric is fluctuating in the range of routine variation, the city and the police department might not know what the effect of the task force is yet. Or, it's possible the task force had no meaningful effect.

Another way data can be misleading is a headline that says, "Homicides in S.A. hit a 21-year high. Why?" There might not be an answer to the question of "Why?" if the number of homicides is still within an established range of the Natural Process Behavior Limits.

The City of San Antonio provides data going back to 2011 on its website. I also found data going back to 2002 from City-data.com, so I created a PBC using 2002 to 2017 data points as the baseline, as shown here:

> When a metric changes, it's important to
> ask and answer the question of "why?" —
> but only when we see a signal.

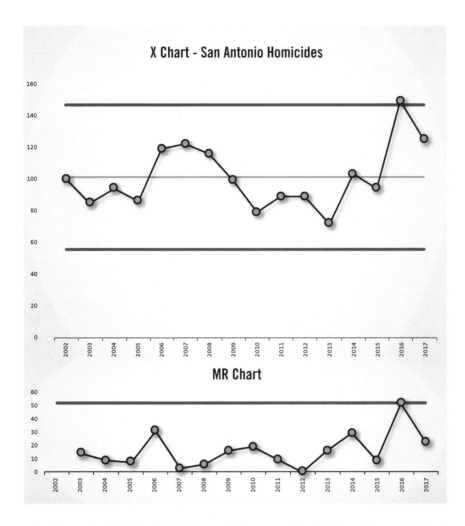

It tells us that 2016, with 149 homicides, was a ***Rule 1*** signal. Instead of asking "Why were homicides 16 percent lower in 2017?" the better question would be about the signal: "Why were homicides so high in 2016?"

It's possible that there was a special cause in 2016, which created the signal and then went away. It's possible that the 2017 data point is now the continuation of the system that was predictable from 2002 to 2015. Or, it's possible that some change in 2016 established a new system that's sustained, with the number of homicides now fluctuating around a higher average. Or, it's possible that the task force yet again changed the system. We don't know for sure from a limited number of data points. We could use monthly data to give us additional data points and limits that will be based on the typical month-to-month variation instead of the year-to-year variation.

We might also choose to look at per capita homicide *rates* over time, since San Antonio's population has grown significantly over the last 20 years.

Below is a PBC showing monthly homicide rates:

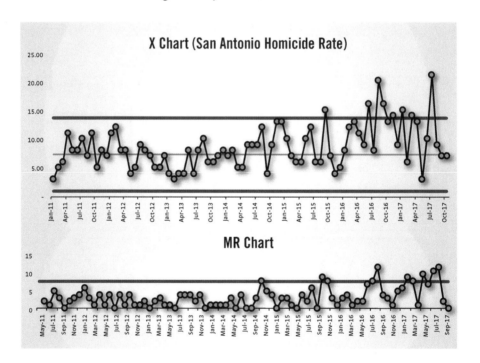

What does the voice of the process tell us through the PBC? We first see a signal (**Rule 1**) in the MR Chart for September 2014 (the MR is 8, compared to the average of 7.7). We also see **Rule 1** signals in both the X Chart and the MR Chart starting in September 2015. We also see **Rule 3** signals, with more than eight consecutive points above the baseline average. It appears that we have a new system.

We can create a revised PBC that shows the starting point of a new system in September 2015. We might not know *what* changed, but the PBC tells us *something* changed. The average homicide rate has increased from 7.3 to 11.0. The amount of routine variation has also increased, which means the spread of the Lower and Upper Limits has increased (and the Lower Limit, although calculated to be negative, gets capped at zero).

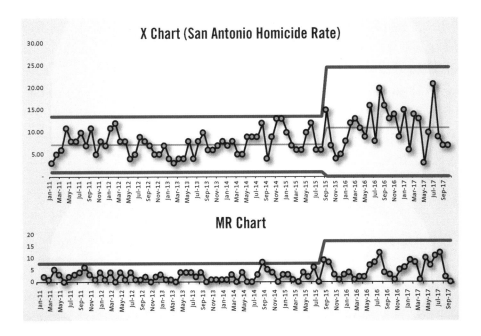

This PBC tells San Antonio that they can predict that the monthly homicide rate will likely fall between zero and 24.8 each month going forward. If their task force started in 2016, I would see no evidence of an additional shift in the system. Either the task force isn't working or it isn't working yet. It can be hard to tell. If we saw eight consecutive points below the new average of 11.0, the city might be able to claim that the task force, or something else, is having a significant impact on homicide rates.

Either the task force isn't working or it isn't working yet. It can be hard to tell.

For now, it's just predictably fluctuating around an average. Some months will be higher than others. There's no reason to ask why a number is different unless one of our three rules gets triggered in the future. Of course, as we talked about in Chapter 4, San Antonio city and police leaders can try to improve the system in a way that lowers the average homicide rate.

Being Dramatic About Oscars Ratings, or a Comedy of Noise?

In 2018, headlines blared about a percentage decrease in viewers for the Academy Awards or how many million fewer viewers there were this year. Many headlines or articles talked about a "record low." Again, if you're tracking a metric, a "record low" or "all-time high" doesn't mean there's a signal to be found. That record low could still be noise in the system. If we were responsible for this system, we'd want to take a more careful look at our metrics to make sure we're not overreacting to a data point that's not meaningful or a perceived trend that doesn't exist.

Here is a headline from the *Wall Street Journal*:

Academy Awards Pull In Record-Low Ratings

Television audience for Oscars on ABC falls 19% to 26.5 million[37]

To their credit, *The Journal* had a chart that showed additional data and context. I've recreated that chart, below. Many news outlets don't show a chart, only giving readers text comparisons, such as ratings being "down 19% from last year's 32.9 million viewers, a nine-year low."

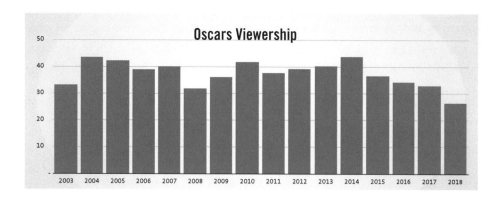

Why did the news report there was an all-time low and a nine-year low? They were reporting two slightly different metrics. The absolute number of viewers was an all-time low, whereas the ratings number (the percentage of televisions tuned into a program) was merely at a nine-year low. The data and charts show that 2018 was the lowest year in recent history by a small margin. But, is that a signal?

The Wall Street Journal used a column chart to show data from 2003 to 2018, as we saw above. As we will discuss in Chapter 7, a Line Chart is a clearer way to visualize time-series data like we have here. *The Journal* sometimes uses Line Charts (aka Run Charts) but not always. Sometimes they use Line Charts and Column Charts side by side in the same article.

Below is the X Chart that I created using data that goes back to 1991 (an arbitrary date that I chose to give additional historical data for the average and limits).

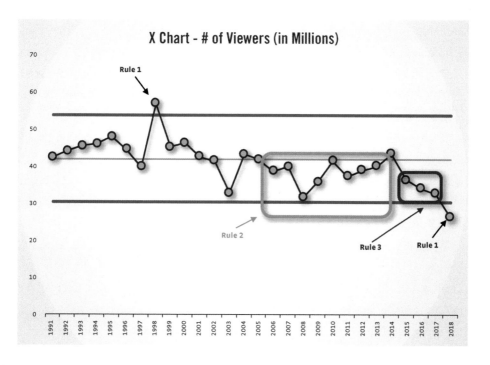

It tells us the number of viewers is not a predictable system over this entire time frame, including 2018. We would not be able to predict future viewership numbers since this chart doesn't reflect a single system over time. The system has changed.

We see multiple signals in the X Chart. There is also one **Rule 1** signal in the MR chart, not shown, that corresponds with the first X Chart signal.

The year 1998 is above the Upper Limit (**Rule 1**). This suggests there is a "special cause" that caused the system to be different that year, even though the results were not sustained. The special cause for the unusually high viewership is commonly thought to be the popularity of the movie *Titanic*, which had 14 nominations that year. The MR Chart has a similar signal at the same time.

There are also eight consecutive data points below the baseline average, a **Rule 2** signal. We also see a cluster of three consecutive points that are closer to the Lower Limit than they are to the average (**Rule 3**).

The year 2018 again falls below the calculated lower limit (**Rule 1**). The Academy would be correct to look for an explanation or a "special cause." Asking about any other single below-average year would likely be a waste of time.

But, the Academy missed an opportunity to start asking "What has changed?" in 2013, when the eighth consecutive below-average data point was found. What led to a downward shift in viewer numbers?

If the number of viewers was fluctuating around an average, then it's unlikely to randomly have eight consecutive points above or below the average. The eighth data point (not the sixth or the seventh) is a signal that something has changed, although it's possible the system changed at the time of the first below-average data point (in 2006).

What is the cause of such a shift? A 2012 *Hollywood Reporter* article points to the now-disgraced Harvey Weinstein pushing smaller-budget "indie" films for awards when those films were far less popular (think the opposite effect of the movie *Titanic*).[38] It seems to suggest that one possible countermeasure for the Academy would be to just nominate the most popular films of the year, but artistic integrity would, hopefully, prevent them from doing that.

The article blamed "the exploding cable TV universe" for the decline in ratings. A systemic change like that could explain the signal of eight consecutive points below the average — and the longer-term trend. The number of TV channels seems to only be increasing. That trend isn't going away.

Other supposed explanations for ups and downs in the chart include:

- Moving the telecast from Monday to Sunday
- Viewers getting used to it being on Sunday
- The hit show *Survivor* was on at the same time
- 9/11
- Other world events
- New producers
- Different hosts

As a reader of this book, you realize that every metric is going to have variation. You'd know not to try to explain every up and down. With viewership numbers fluctuating around an average, the Academy could end up in a cycle where they name a new celebrity host and see ratings go up. So, they'd bring the host back again and see ratings decline. The Academy might conclude that the public has tired of the host, leading them to hire somebody else.

Dr. W. Edwards Deming might have used the term "tampering" to describe that scramble for possible solutions. He'd say that tampering with a predictable system would generally increase variation in the system and the metric. Instead of making thoughtful changes based on knowledge of the system, the Academy might be trying random changes that just lead to more random fluctuation, which then causes them to draw the wrong conclusions about what works and what doesn't.

Getting back to the PBC, I redrew the Process Behavior Chart to show where a shift seemed to occur in 2006, shown below. If we are discovering an emergent shift in the process, we might essentially be guessing when the new process began. An educated guess for when a shift below the old system's average began is the first data point below the old average.

The new average for the new system, with a baseline of 2006 to 2018, is 36.9 million viewers, with Lower and Upper Limits of 26.5 and 47.3, as shown below:

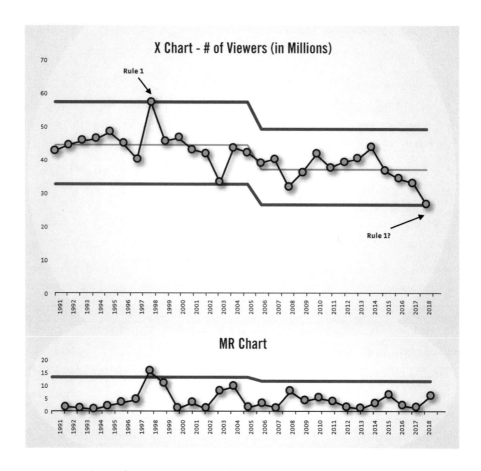

The number of viewers used to fluctuate around an average of 42.27 million viewers. The old system was predictable in that the number of viewers would have been expected to fall between the limits of 30.5 and 54.07 million viewers. We would have expected that system to remain predictable until something changed in the system — whether that's a one-time event (*Titanic*) or a technology shift (hundreds of TV channels).

The year 2018 appears to be right on the cusp of being a special cause (***Rule 1***). It's right on the Lower Limit line. The calculated Lower Limit is 26.50 and, with rounding, the number of viewers was reported as 26.5. Instead of worrying about whether it's precisely above or below the limit, we can treat it as a special cause, accepting the small risk that the data point is noise instead of a signal. It would most likely be appropriate for the Academy to ask "why were ratings low in 2018?"

Again, the Academy missed a chance to ask something like "what changed in 2006 or so that caused the average viewership to drop to an average of 36.9 million viewers?" They could have detected this shift in 2013 when they would have seen the eighth consecutive point below the old average.

What is the special cause of that sustained shift downward? If the Academy could have identified what changed, it's possible they could have taken counter-measures to address it. On the other hand, if the special cause was a broader societal or technological trend, they probably couldn't take action. We'll never go back to a day of having just seven or eight channels available.

Since 2018 was the fourth consecutive year below the newest average, it's possible this is the beginning of ANOTHER shift (some say it's due to the rise of Netflix this time). But, the four data points alone are not a signal.

If we have four more years below 37.4 million viewers or if the number falls below 26.5 in 2019 (or any other future year), we'd see a signal worth investigating.

Is Ratings Percentage a Better Metric?

The number of viewers matters, but part of the context of that metric is that the U.S. population (and the global television audience) is growing each year. Another metric used in the television business is the "Ratings Percentage," or the percentage of televisions that are tuned into a program. This metric scales with population growth and might be better comparison metric over time.

A PBC for the Ratings Percentage shows a similar spike for 'Titanic" in 1998 and a similar *Rule 2* run below the average, starting in 2005:

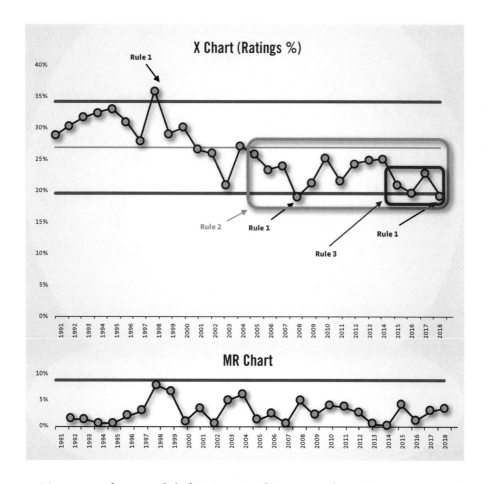

There was a downward shift in 2005, and it appears the ratings percentage has been stable and predictable since that shift occurred. In cases like this, it's hard to know *exactly* when the system changed, when discovering an emergent shift in the average, but there clearly was a shift, as shown in the next chart:

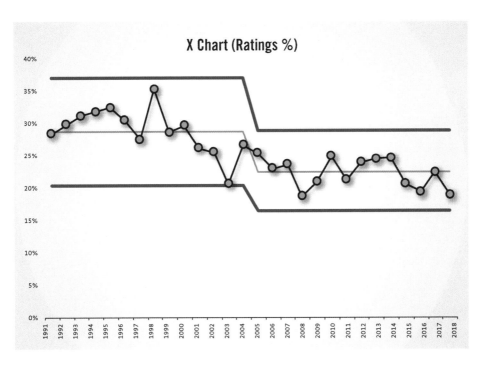

If it has been a new predictable system since 2005, then we'd conclude there's no reason to ask "Why were ratings down in 2018?" since that data point represents noise — it's part of the routine variation in the new system.

What can we learn from headlines and stories like this? Hopefully, they help us become more savvy consumers of the news — and more savvy consumers of charts and metrics in our workplaces.

For additional case studies and blog posts about data from the news, see my blog via this URL: https://www.leanblog.org/tag/pbc-case-studies/. I will add more case studies and examples over time.

CHAPTER 7

Linear Trend Lines and Other Cautionary Tales

I n the absence of the Process Behavior Chart methodology, organizations use other methods in their attempts to explain performance metrics and drive improvement. Unfortunately, some of these methods are misleading or lacking in some way. In this chapter, we compare PBCs to other methods and further explore the problems with what might be "the way we've always done it." We can't fault people for what they don't know or for doing what they were taught, but we can strive to improve the way we improve.

Data Have No Meaning Without Context

Revisiting Key Point #3, "No data have meaning apart from their context," how often do we see a number, a metric, or a chart that seems to have no context?

Wheeler writes:

1. "Trust no one who cannot, or will not, provide the context for their figures.
2. Stop reporting comparisons between pairs of values except as part of a broader comparison.
3. Start using graphs to present current values in context."

Once in a hospital, I saw that leaders had posted some performance measures in the lobby for the public to see, a laudable attempt at transparency. Unfortunately, the data likely didn't have any meaning to the general public (or to hospital employees, I would imagine).

The one piece of data that stood out, in particular, is pictured below:

Quality Panel Score	
YTD Actual	3.58
YTD Target	3.59

What do those numbers mean to the general public? Is the hospital helping or informing anyone through the posting of these numbers?

What context is missing? Without the proper context, the display begs the questions:

- What is a "quality panel"? Is this like the show *Dancing With the Stars*, where a panel is scoring quality?
- What's the maximum (best) score? Is the score 3.58 out of 5 or out of 10?
- What is the trend over the past few years (as opposed to just comparing the actual current number to the target)?
- How does this score compare to other hospitals? Is 3.58 a good score or a bad score?
- How is this score indicative of the risks to patients or their outcomes?

I'd also ask why the target was set as 3.59. Did they plan to have less than perfect quality (whatever "perfect" would be)? Why is the actual so suspiciously close to the target? If the target were 4.5, would we see an actual of 4.49? Are people manipulating the data in some way?

When I see a target like 3.58, I cringe when I think about how many minutes, if not hours, were spent debating or arguing if the target should be 3.58, 3.59, 3.5, or 4.0. What would happen if time spent selecting a target were, instead, invested into improving the system and, therefore, improving its performance? Is the ultimate goal 5.0?

Why do they even need a target? Would the lack of a target hamper people's efforts at delivering the best patient care? How does the target help improve quality? Does the target become, in effect, a limit to this year's improvement?

It would be much more helpful to plot this quality panel score over time as a PBC. This would allow us to see how much the score varies over time, if it's hitting the target some or most of the time, and if the score is improving or not. Having some context about how this score compares to other hospitals would also help (although our goal should be perfect quality, not beating benchmarks or targets).

If the hospital plotted its monthly quality panel score, staff should also be mindful of not overreacting to every small blip up and down in that metric over time.

Are We Fooling Ourselves About Improvement?

To create and sustain a culture of improvement, we need to honestly evaluate our changes to see if they are indeed improvements. In many organizations, however, there is pressure to *prove* that our attempt at improvement was a success when fear reigns over science. People are often pressured to paint a picture of positive results instead of looking for evidence of significant improvement.

It's difficult to tell sometimes if a person is intentionally misleading you through charts and graphs or if they just haven't been taught more valid methods and best practices. "Hanlon's Razor" isn't the most polite expression, but it says, "Never attribute to malice that which is adequately explained by stupidity." Maybe it's more accurate to say, "Never attribute to malice that which is adequately explained by not knowing the best methods."

People often try representing their improvement work this way, though. We might see a chart like this in an improvement summary presentation:

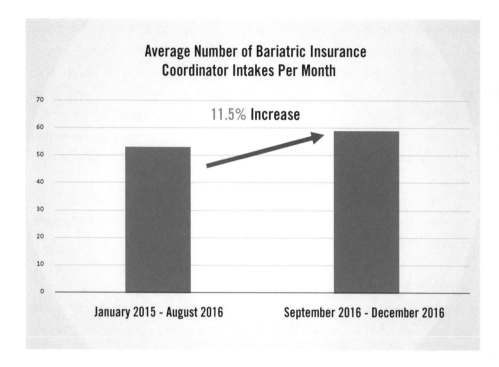

They claim an 11.5% increase. But I wouldn't accept the analysis on face value. I'd push back and ask them to plot the dots; get the actual data for each month and create a PBC. Their approach to visualizing the data compares the average of 19 months (the before) with an average of just four months (the after).

It's possible that an 11.5% increase is just noise. Without the context of a PBC, we cannot tell if they are claiming victory based on noise in the data.

In another example, I saw a consulting case study that was published online a few years ago. The headline trumpeted cost savings, and a bullet point in the case study read, "The average patient satisfaction increased from 87.2 to 89%." How do we know if that's signal or noise?

To their credit, the consultants provided a Run Chart that looked like this:

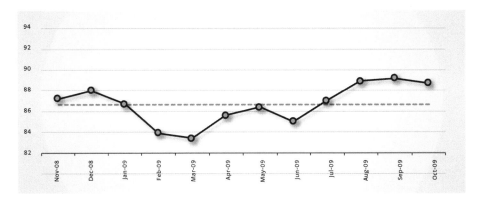

They added the line for the average of 86.8. Just looking at the chart using the PBC lens, I'm not certain if patient satisfaction *improved* or if it's fluctuating around the average.

While the case study explains **what** was done in the attempt to improve patient satisfaction, the timing for this intervention or change to the system is unclear. Did the improvement take place in November 2008, with the first data point in the chart being portrayed as the baseline of the old system?

In their two-data-point comparison that paints a picture of improvement, the consultants chose the first and last data points. A better comparison would use the Process Behavior Chart method to show if there is a signal of a change to the system and a shift in performance:

If the consultants had collected data only through June 2009, their "first and last" data point method would tell a different story:

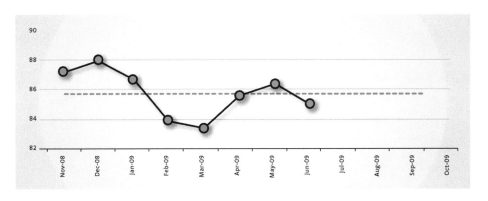

Their case study bullet point would then have to read, "The average patient satisfaction *decreased* from 87.2 to 85%." But, that story wouldn't sell more consulting work. A PBC would look like this:

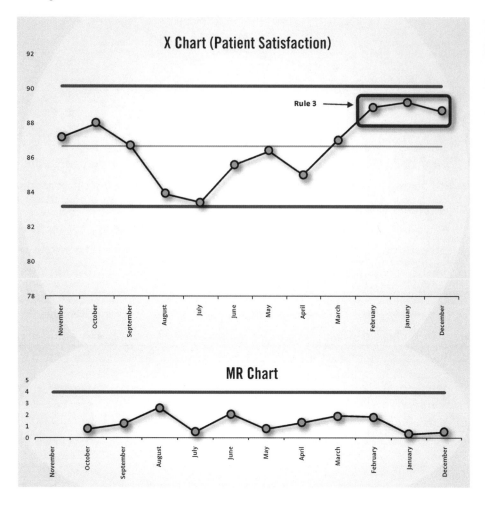

The only evidence of a possible sustained shift in performance is the last three data points, a **Rule 3** signal. We could be more confident that an upward shift had occurred once we see another five months that are all also above the average (**Rule 2**). That would be evidence that a new system had been established.

We could not yet definitively say patient satisfaction "improved to 89%" because the voice of the process gives no evidence that it will always (or sometimes) be 89% or higher. The PBC would suggest that the patient satisfaction score in November 2009 and beyond is likely to be between the Natural Process Limits 83% and 90% unless we see stronger evidence of the system changing.

In looking at charts that aim to show the result of an intervention, there are two other good practices to add to our approach:

KEY POINT #9: If there was an intervention in the system, make it clear in your chart or your discussion of the chart when that change was started or implemented.

We also want to make sure we don't mislead the reader of the chart by showing just a single "before" data point. It's helpful to show the context of additional data points that illustrate the old system as a range of results with inherent routine variation, as expressed by an old average and old Natural Process Limits.

KEY POINT #10: When showing the "before" scenario, show enough data points to illustrate the previous level of variation, not just a single data point.

Below is a good example of an X Chart that illustrates Key Points #9 and #10:

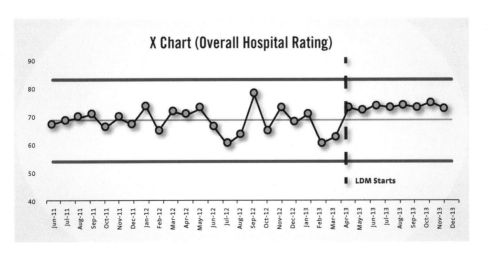

We can see the baseline data and how the overall rating score fluctuated around an average of about 70%. The PBC allows us to predict that future scores after February 2013 would likely be between about 57 and 82 — unless we improved the system.

The chart shows when their new "Lean Daily Management" system started. It's encouraging that the first eight data points are above the baseline average, a **Rule 2** signal that the system has indeed changed. We could then recalculate the average and the limits. We'd see a higher average and narrower limits since the point-to-point variation has decreased.

That might not paint the picture that management or their internal Lean coaching staff might want to tell (the new average is only about 73), but it would be a more accurate view than using the first and last data points to "prove" that a certain level of improvement had occurred. It would be more accurate than cherry-picking any two data points to show a before-and-after comparison that's favorable to them.

Missing Signals Because of Red/Green Analysis

Think of a situation in a call center, where the metric "call abandonment rate" is measured. Management has set a target of 10% because they've somehow deemed that to be an acceptable level of performance. Every day, the team sees the previous day's rate written on a whiteboard. If the number is below 10%, it's written in green.

The assumption is that if the day is better than the target, then everything is fine and there's nothing to discuss. To answer our **Question 1**, the team is hitting the target on a particular day. We can't tell if we are doing so consistently without a chart or something that shows trends.

What would happen if the team had a Run Chart for this daily performance that looked like this?

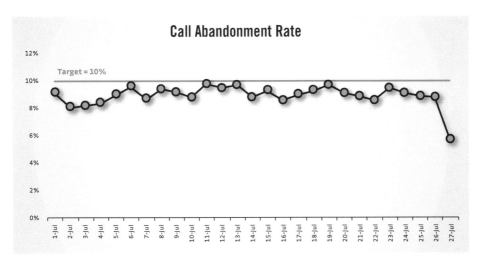

On that last day, the rate seems noticeably lower. The rate had been previously fluctuating between 8% and 10%, so they were consistently better than their target.

In their red/green approach to management, nobody would react and talk about the process unless the rate was above the target of 10%. Likewise, a day that was significantly better didn't draw much attention and didn't lead to any discussion.

Of course, if we create a PBC for this data, it tells us more than the Run Chart:

We can't tell if we are hitting our target consistently
without a chart or something that shows trends.

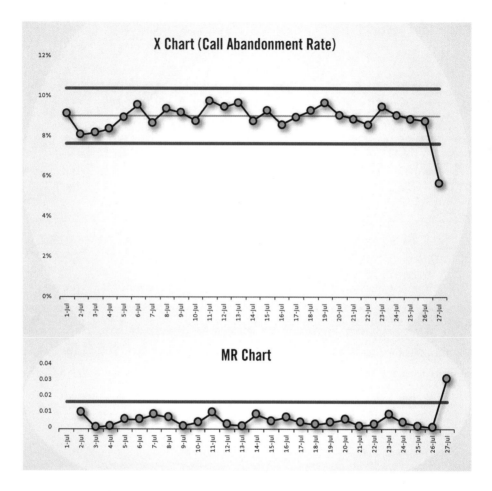

There is a clear **_Rule 1_** signal on both the X Chart and the MR Chart. This data point is still "green," but it's a signal that's worth discussing. Does the call center know why the rate was suddenly lower than the PBC would have predicted from the system? It's unlikely that there was a 6% rate one day due to chance alone. The previous system couldn't have produced those results. Something changed. The organization would lose an important opportunity to learn if they treated the 5.7% green day the same as the previous green days.

After one day, we don't know yet if this day was a fluke (perhaps due to some-thing out of our control that's unlikely to be repeated) or if this day could poten-tially be the start of sustained and improved performance.

If the call center can discover and understand what change had been made to their system, they can try to lock in that performance by making it the new standardized method. Without a PBC, they might have missed out on noticing that, perhaps, a team member did an experiment about the way calls were assigned. Missing that signal means a lost opportunity to lock in better performance.

We'd hope to then see performance like the chart below over time, with eight consecutive points below the old average (***Rule 2***), further strengthening the case that performance has improved, as we establish a new average and limits for the chart. The system is now predictably performing at a better rate. It's better than the 10% target like it was before, but now performance is much improved.

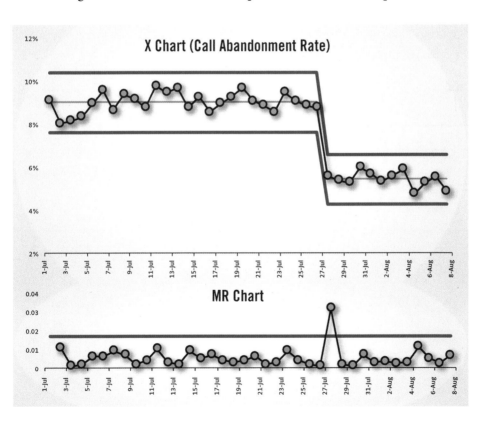

Do We Want to Meet Targets? Or Improve?

In the hospital quality panel score scenario, the target was suspiciously close to the actual number. If we have a culture of improvement, we're less afraid to set a challenging goal, since we have a method of working together to improve. In this culture, people aren't blamed or punished for the existence of this gap between actual and target.

The tension or gap between actual and target is resolved by improving the system (not by telling people to try harder or to care more). Of course, if we don't have a methodology for improvement, the organization might be very uncomfortable with that sort of tension. When that's the case, we get targets that are the same or just slightly better than the previous year. People might resolve that tension by fudging the numbers or distorting the system.

In my travels, I've seen customer satisfaction survey data posted at airports, including Dallas-Fort Worth (DFW) and London Heathrow. A sign from DFW, as recreated below, shows some results that are suspiciously close to the target at the different terminals:

RESTAURANT / EATING FACILITIES

TERMINAL	RATING	TARGET
A	3.9	4.0
B	3.9	3.9
C	3.9	3.9
D	4.2	4.2
E	3.9	3.9
DFW	4.0	4.0

It makes me wonder why the target for terminals A and D is higher than the other three terminals. Is the target higher for terminal D because it's the international terminal and those passengers have higher expectations? Again, I also wonder how much time went into debating those specific targets.

The data also lack context. Is 5.0 the best possible score, as implied by the blue shading in the rating? What are these ratings over time?

Did the manager of Terminal A lose out on a bonus for missing the target by 0.1? Are the other terminals supposed to stop improving because they hit their targets? Wouldn't it be more helpful to talk about *what* they are doing instead of just showing how they are measuring this? I'd feel more assured that quality improvement was coming if they gave at least one cause or reason for the scores not being higher. That might demonstrate some understanding of the system.

These targets are set in a way that does not create any tension or drive for improvement. Is this the best that DFW and their food providers can do? What improvements could be made to their system to drive better performance?

In organizations with an improvement culture, they would set the long-term goal to be 5.0, if that's the best possible score. To help drive incremental improvement, the organization might set an intermediate target of, say, 4.5. Leaders wouldn't necessarily expect immediate perfection but setting a target that creates positive tension can be helpful, but if, and only if, leaders provide support and guidance that create an environment where improvement can occur.

Since sustainable systemic improvement requires analysis, leaders at DFW would have to understand reasons for the created gap. Are the scores lower than 5.0 because of food selection, food quality, waiting times, seating availability, or other factors?

During a recent trip through Heathrow, I saw the display of results that are, again, suspiciously close to the targets (the dashed red line), as recreated below. Were the targets based on last year's results? It appears that the primary aim of airport management is to "be green" instead of driving improvement to a higher level.

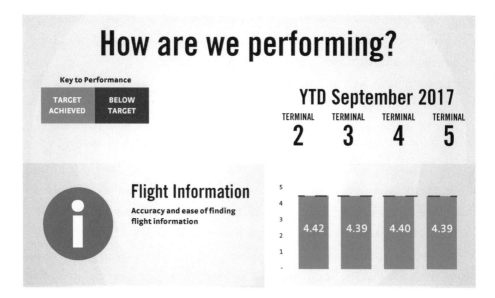

At one hospital I visited, their chart for an employee injury metric had a target added (in green); it was suspiciously close to the average level of recent performance:

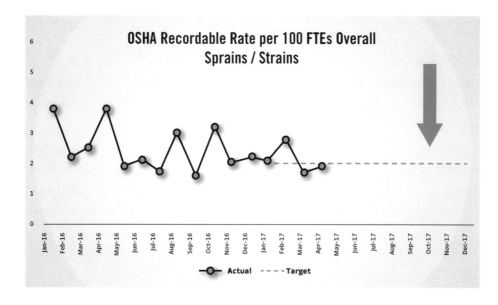

In a case like this, if performance continues to remain predictable, then this organization was setting itself up for a situation where they would go between green and red almost continually. The ultimate goal for this metric would be zero. If they had set an intermediate target of 1 sprain or strain per 100 employees instead of 2, that would have created a tension that drives improvement.

An X Chart, shown below, helps us hear the voice of the process that says the system will generate a metric lower than 2.0 occasionally, even if we do nothing to improve the system.

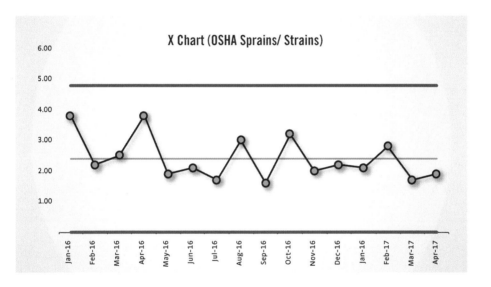

The PBC shows us any result between the limits of 0.01 and 4.80 is noise. The chart tells us it's unrealistic to always be lower than the target without making significant improvements.

Improving the system and lowering the number of sprains and strains requires an understanding of the system that identifies common causes of those problems over time. Looking at September 2016 and asking "Why was the metric so good that month?" is unlikely to give us a meaningful answer. Yes, that month shows it's possible to have fewer than two sprains and strains, but it's unlikely that anything was being done differently that month.

Line Charts vs. Column Charts

Why do so many organizations use what's often called "Bar Charts" to display time series data? Excel can take some of the blame, as it nudges you to create what it calls "Column Charts," by listing that option first in the menus before Line Charts.

A typical Column Chart looks like this, in an example of a daily patient flow metric:

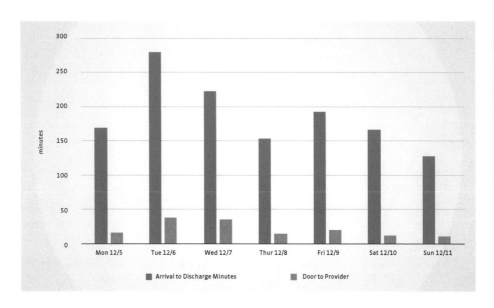

It's better to see any form of chart than a table of numbers. But, Line Charts are easier to read and require fewer mental gymnastics on the part of the reader.

Line Charts are, for one, easier to draw by hand if you're creating a simple chart in the workplace. Secondly, Line Charts make it easier to see trends, especially when they are the basis for Process Behavior Charts.

I agree with James M. Smith, Ph.D., who writes the following in his helpful book *Meaningful Graphs* (with my emphasis added):

"**Column charts are primarily used to convey data on discrete categories (hospitals, wards, clinics, etc.). They can also be used to display data over time periods but only for a *limited number of time periods* [up to 8].**"[39]

Here are two separate Run Charts of the patient flow data from the combined column chart from above, where the lines and the scale make the graph easier to read and interpret.

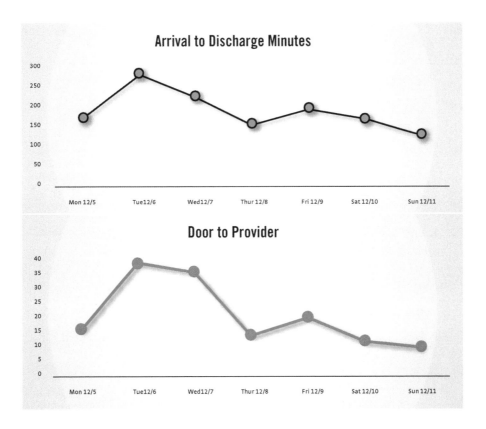

Below is an example of a more appropriate use of a Column Chart that compares the ratings of different physicians at a point in time.

Smith also writes:

"Line charts are ideal for showing trends over time or successive events. They can be used for either short or long time periods."

It's important to remember:

- If you have data plotted over time, use a Line Chart.
- If you are comparing data across people or sites at a point in time, use a Column Chart.

When they are used to show a time series (or, in this next case, two), Column Charts do more than waste printer ink. They hide and mask trends that we need to carefully evaluate and use for reacting appropriately. Our eyes are drawn to the middle of the shaded column when the data point of interest is at the top of the column. Using dots and connecting them with lines makes the data and trends more easily apparent.

Many of the apps that we use on a daily basis use Column Charts for a time series when I wish they would use a Line Chart. For example, my wearable fitness tracker displays sleep data over time as a Column Chart over a three-month period, which looks similar to this:

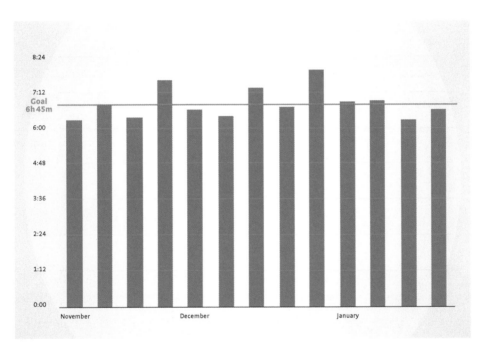

The target that I've set for my average sleep time is 6 hours and 45 minutes. It's arbitrary, but it's realistic as a nightly target and, in my judgment, I operate best on between 6.5 and 7 hours of sleep.

My long-term average is 6 hours and 57 minutes. Am I meeting my target? Yes, sometimes. That's true for individual nights and the weeks shown in this chart. Am I improving and becoming more consistent? It is hard to determine this from a Column Chart.

If I convert this to an X Chart, I get the visual benefits of a Run Chart with the additional benefits of the average and the limits, as shown below:

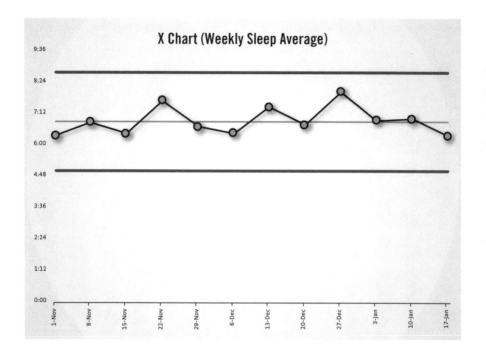

The Line Chart format is much easier to read. The X Chart tells me that, given my routine variation, I'd expect my weekly sleep average to be anywhere between about five hours and 8.5 hours. I shouldn't overreact to changes in my sleep unless I see a signal.

Be Careful With Linear Trend Lines

People often add a linear trend line to their Run Charts. This is very easy to do in Microsoft Excel, requiring literally just two clicks. But, "easy" doesn't mean it is helpful.

Unfortunately, linear trend lines can be misleading, as they imply that performance will continue on the trajectory shown by the line. This implied hypothesis of continued improvement (or decline) in a metric might not be realistic.

When a PBC predicts future performance within the range of our Natural Process Limits, it's more reasonable to assume that a predictable system remains

predictable. The linear trend line's prediction is based on a hypothesis of continued steady change, something a PBC can also identify.

Let's look at the Run Chart of a customer satisfaction metric, with survey
scores that can fall between zero and 100%. The linear trend line is in red:

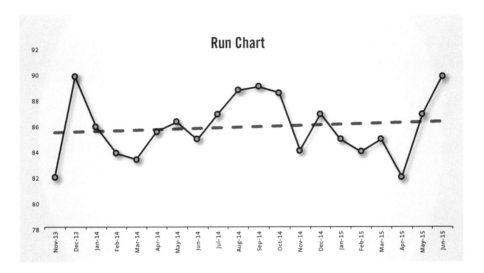

Is the metric improving? After learning about PBCs, you would look at a
chart like this differently. Is customer satisfaction fluctuating around an average?
A linear trend line implies we are improving, as it goes up and to the right.

One problem with linear trend lines is that they can be highly sensitive to the
oldest and the most recent data points. For example, if we charted the exact same
data from above, but this time removing the first and last data point, our linear
trend line tells the opposite story:

Linear trend lines can be misleading, as they imply that
performance will continue on the trajectory shown by the line.

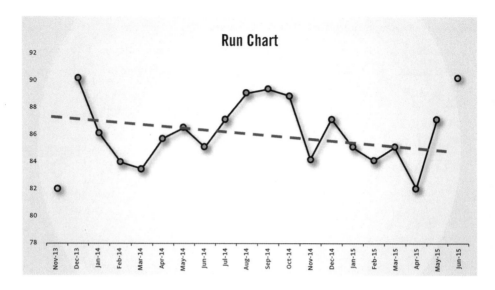

Oops! It's now down and to the right. How can what's essentially the same data set be increasing *and* decreasing over roughly the same time frames? It's possible because the metric is the result of a predictable system, as we see in this X Chart for the data from November 2013 to June 2015:

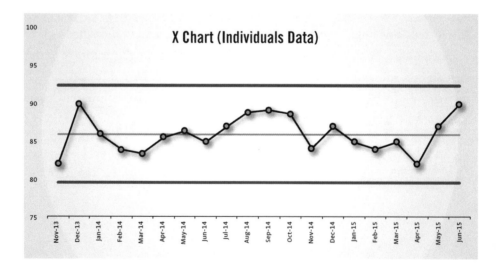

None of our three rules are triggered. Instead of hoping that the metric will continue improving, the PBC allows us to predict that customer satisfaction will fall between 79.5% and 92.5%, unless we can improve the system. We'd use, of course, our three rules as evidence of change.

A Process Behavior Chart is less sensitive to our starting and ending points in the data set, which means it's less likely to be misunderstood or inadvertently (or intentionally) abused.

If we remove the first and last data points, the PBC still shows a predictable system. The voice of the process, as expressed by the PBC, is more consistent than the linear trend line approach. The average and the limits are slightly different, but we'd draw the same conclusion from this PBC. And drawing accurate conclusions from our data is a key step for people who want to be part of an effective improvement process.

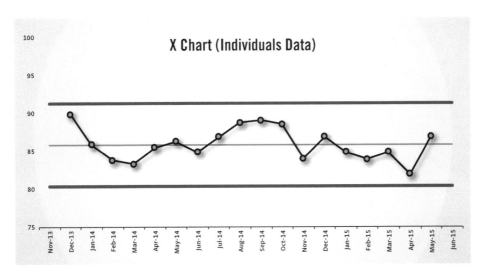

Linear trend lines might describe what happened in the past, but they don't make a valid prediction about future performance as well as a predictable PBC does. The linear trend line may mistakenly give the impression that the metric will keep improving on its own, eventually hitting 100%.

It's more accurate to look at improvements over time as a series of step function changes on a PBC — we improve the system, performance goes up to a new average, and we repeat.

The first linear trend line shown earlier implies that performance will continually increase at a relatively slow pace. We could run a calculation for how many years out it would be before the metric hits 100%. We should focus our efforts, instead, on figuring out how to improve the system.

The chart below shows additional data with a linear trend line that covers the longer time period. This line has a steeper slope, implying a faster rate of improvement. But, the line incorrectly implies we had steady, consistent improvement. The line also suggests the impossible — that performance will soon exceed 100%:

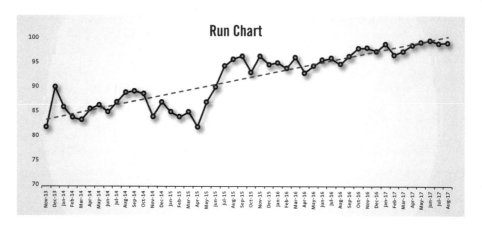

Did the metric improve at the same pace each month? An X Chart showing shifts in the average and limits more accurately reflects what happened.

We see predictable performance for a period and then improvement to a higher level of predictable performance. Then, another improvement to an even higher level. We see two **Rule 2** signals of eight consecutive points above the previous average. Instead of truly continuous improvement, there are two shifts in the system — and a third shift may soon be seen if we get three more consecutive data points above this third average.

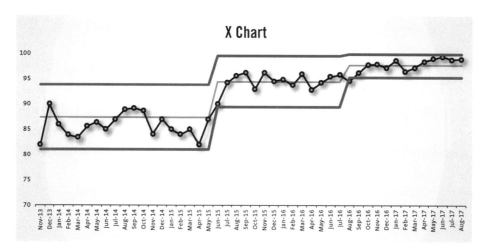

We can use the X Chart to predict that customer satisfaction will vary between 95.3% and 100% going forward, unless something changes yet again. The linear trend line wouldn't tell us that.

Why Start Each Year With a Blank Chart?

As we plot a metric each month, we'll see 10 or 11 data points by the end of the year (depending on how much the compilation or posting of the metric lags). Those data points provide helpful context, even if the chart is drawn as a Column Chart:

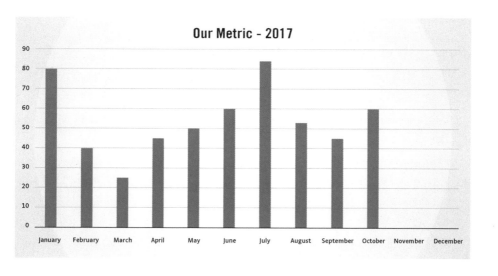

Many organizations would then, in January, post a blank chart to start the new year. Why would we throw away the additional context of data from 2016 when we start the 2017 chart in January?

It's unlikely that January 1st in any given year is the magical creation of a new system. In other words, January 2017 likely starts with the same process we had at the end of December 2016. The annual cutoffs are arbitrary. Sure, people are accustomed to thinking in annual cycles, but is this helpful for improvement?

When we then get a chart with one data point (January), we can, at best, compare that data point against a target. We can do better, with charts that continue to show some data from the previous year.

Below is a Run Chart that Amazon provides to me, with weekly book sales:

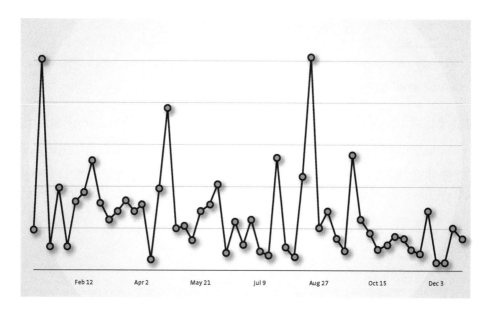

With the start of the new year, I wouldn't want to see a blank chart with only one or two data points as January starts and progresses.

Thankfully, Amazon adds new data points to the chart. I can choose to view the last 52 weeks. As we add a data point, the oldest data point is dropped. I can also view "all historical data" for even more context, if I choose (which is what I normally look at).

This next chart, showing the last 51 weeks of the previous year, with the additional first data point of the next year, is helpful:

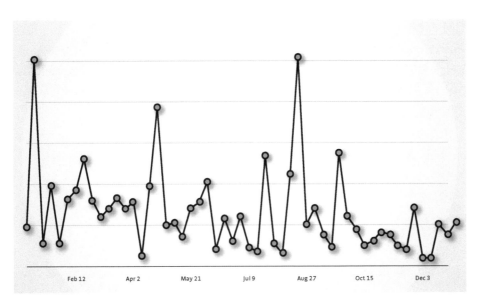

This alternative chart, with just one data point displayed for the new year, is not as helpful:

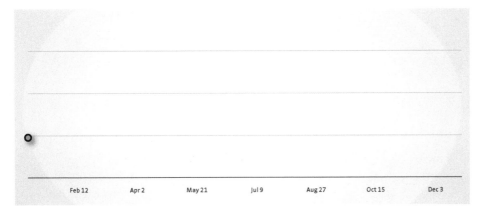

If part of the purpose of having a metric is to ask "are we improving?" then you shouldn't throw out the previous year's data in a big batch at the start of the year.

The start of a new year is most likely the continuation of last year's system. Your charts and metrics should reflect that.

Year-Over-Year Charts

Since our systems and improvement efforts tend to continue across annual boundaries, it's helpful to display two years' worth of data on a chart. This is particularly true if we have a monthly metric, where 24 data points provide helpful context and a baseline for evaluating trends or shifts in performance.

I see many organizations post a chart that shows the data from two consecutive years as two different lines that are laid over each other, as shown below:

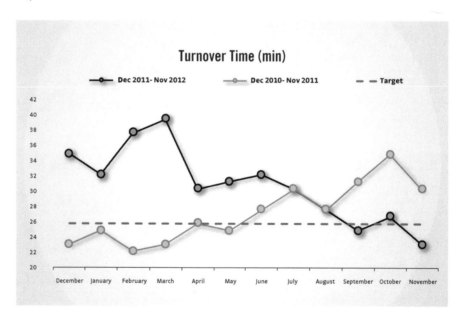

This chart is hard to read because some of the data points on the two lines overlap (in July and August). Its legend (underneath the title) confuses the reader by showing 12-month periods that don't go from January to January, as we might typically expect, and by listing the most recent year first.

Can charts like this help answer our core questions?

Question 1: Are we achieving our target or goal?

At a glance, it appears that there were more data points in 2011 below the target of 25 minutes than there were in 2012. But, performance at the end of the second year has reached the target again. There appear to be more data points above the target than below. So it seems not to be at the desired level.

Question 2: Are we improving?

I find it difficult to read the trend over time with the stacked lines. A chart like the one above is most useful if we are looking for seasonality in data, to see if there is a repeated pattern each year. It looks like the performance got worse and then improved.

It's much easier to read and interpret a Run Chart with a single line or a Process Behavior Chart. The Run Chart from that data looks like this:

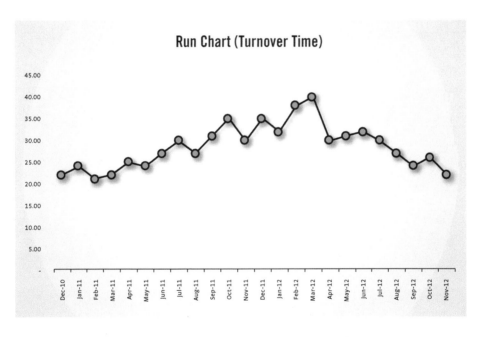

The up-and-down trend over the two years is more clear when it's plotted as a single line. This chart also has a vertical axis that starts at zero, to give a more appropriate scale to the chart and the data. Compared to the original chart, this chart more accurately shows the opportunity for improvement to potentially reduce the turnaround time to less than 20 minutes.

As Smith writes:

> **"One of the first rules of charts is that if you have to do any mental gymnastics to get the information you want from a chart, it's not a good chart."**[40]

An X Chart for this data looks like this (where the MR Chart, not displayed, has no signals):

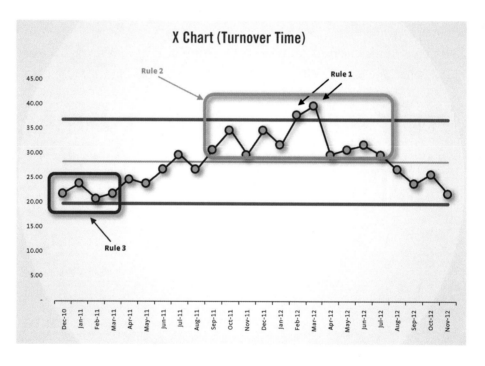

What signals do we see? First, there are 11 consecutive data points above the average *(Rule 2)*, starting in September 2011. Secondly, we have data points above the Upper Limit *(Rule 1)*. This is not a predictable system. We also find a few *Rule 3* signals. In the MR Chart, the highest data point is below the Upper Range Limit, so it's not a signal.

We can ask, "What was different from September 2011 to August 2012?" What caused the average turnaround time to shift from an average of 25 minutes to an average of 32 minutes? Did that cause disappear in September 2012? Has performance been restored to its previous level? Was it because of a change we made to the system? Or, did we discover the apparent downward shift in the data that leads us to investigate a cause?

Since the metric does not show a predictable system, it's hard to predict what performance would be in December 2012 and other future months. We could represent two shifts in the system in this chart:

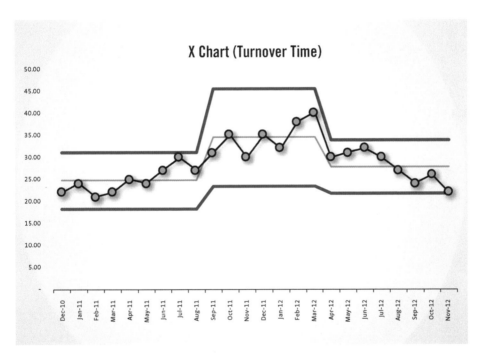

X Chart (Turnover Time)

We have three different systems over time. Starting in September 2010, the average was 25. Starting in September 2011, we even see ***Rule 1 and Rule 2*** signals, which tells us the system has changed and it then fluctuated for about a year around an average of 31. Then, starting in April 2012, we see a run of eight consecutive points below that second average (***Rule 2***), which suggest a shift down to an average of about 28.

We don't know what changed or got worse in that shift from the first average to the second, higher average. When the average number of falls went back down the chart alone won't tell us if the problem or circumstances that led to the increase went away or if that problem still exists and another improvement was made that countered the effect.

When in doubt, plot the dots, and look to see what the voice of the process is saying. The process is talking to you. The question is, "Are you listening?"

CHAPTER 8

Workplace Cases and Examples

n this chapter, we'll see examples of Process Behavior Charts being used to evaluate tests of change and the performance of various systems. The focus is on the management mindsets that we would employ when using PBCs, with comparisons to the typical approaches we might see before PBCs being adopted.

Are Employees at a Japanese Company Submitting Fewer Ideas?

At a Japanese company, leaders were proud that employees had participated in a Total Quality Management (TQM) program for more than two decades. In recent years, staff were able to supplement the six-month TQM projects with "small kaizens," where *kaizen* is a Japanese word that means "continuous improvement."[41] All of these improvements followed the PDSA cycle that was mentioned in Chapter 4.

Leaders were worried, however, that the number of submitted small kaizens fell from 138 to 58. The presentation from senior leadership showed sad and shame-filled cartoon faces. Was that decrease worth reacting to?

The presentation showed a Column Chart with 10 data points, which could also be displayed as a PBC, as shown below:

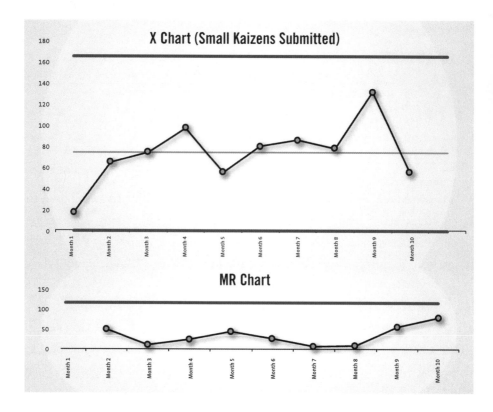

Even a Run Chart without limits would put the last month's decline into better context. The big decrease followed a significant increase the month before. Instead of asking only, "Why did the number drop in Month 10?" management might also be tempted to ask, "Why did the number go up so much in Month 9?"

Actually, neither of those is the right question in this situation as, thankfully, the PBC Chart provides even more context. With our calculated Natural Process Limits, we shouldn't react to any of those single data points. So far, this is a predictable system that will likely generate between zero and 167 ideas in Month 11, unless leaders can improve the system.

If leaders want to see more participation in the "small kaizen" program, they should step back and figure out how to improve the system. They might follow the A3 problem-solving process, as we introduced in Chapter 4.

The company formed a panel to work on this challenge. They mapped the current situation with a process flow diagram. That's better than jumping to solutions that aren't sustainable, such as offering raffles and prizes for people who submit ideas.

Leaders brainstormed more than a dozen different causes of low kaizen participation. They concluded there was no single root cause, as we would expect in a system that has nothing but routine variation. They came up with three countermeasures to test:

- Increase the number of announcements about the "Small Kaizen Contest"
- Improve the kaizen sheet (they thought "the old form was difficult to write")
- Posting a "Kaizen Box" (to make them "easier to submit")

Their presentation showed just one new data point after those changes were made. The number went up to 94 in Month 11, and the presentation showed joyful cartoon faces. Unfortunately, this was still within the range of routine variation. There was no signal of a large change in the system or its performance — at least not yet — as seen in the X Chart, below:

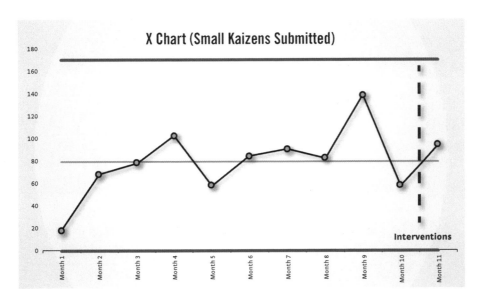

The company could continue with those three countermeasures, as additional communication might eventually spur more participation. It's hard to tell sometimes if an idea we have implemented isn't working or just isn't working yet. They could try additional countermeasures, accepting the downside that it might cloud their cause-and-effect evaluation.

To prove that an idea had a large impact, they could look for a **Rule 1** signal. If they have boosted the average number of kaizens, the hospital would look for **Rule 2** or **Rule 3** signals. Here is a scenario that shows all three of those signals, as illustrated below:

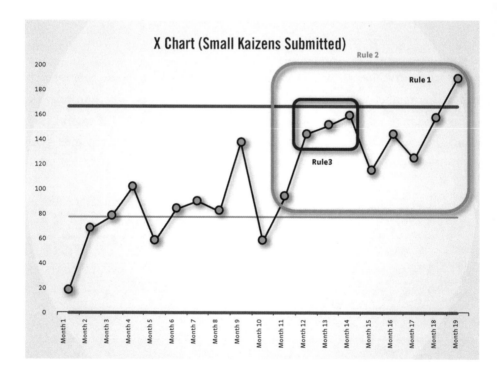

That performance increase suggests a new system exists, with an average and limits that are higher than before:

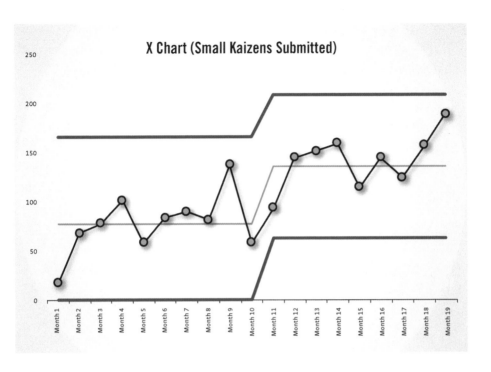

The new limits would tell leaders they can expect the next months to bring between 63 and 210 submissions unless the system changes again. And, if they choose, they can continue working to boost participation, and the PBC can be used to evaluate their results. It's great to see a company applying the kaizen process to their small kaizen system.

Are These Hospitals Reducing Patient Falls?

The next scenario is from a health system. A nursing executive with responsibility for improving multiple facilities entered the room saying, "I need to show a 30% reduction in falls. That's our national target. Can you help me show this?"

My first thought was, "I don't know. We need to hear what the voice of the process is saying."

The executive was focused on the voice of the customer, if you consider management (or political leaders) to be the customer of her work. The actual voice of the patients might say, "None of us want to fall and get injured. The ultimate goal should be zero."

The executive had data from multiple facilities, so we had to hear what each process was saying. Let's plot the dots and see what PBCs help us understand.

Facility #1

For the first facility, the previous year's weekly average had been 44 falls, which meant their 30% reduction target would bring that number down to 31 (and she agreed the longer-term goal was zero). The executive brought a Run Chart that had two horizontal lines: the previous year's average and the target:

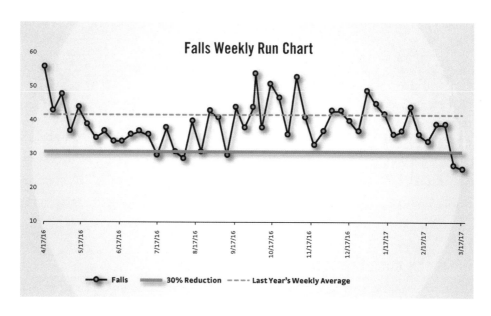

What does the Run Chart tell us?

- There are some weeks that had fewer than 31 falls
- The number of falls fluctuates
- In some weeks there are more falls than the previous year's average

The Run Chart can't tell us what we would predict going forward, as a PBC could.

The chart also doesn't indicate when (or if) any interventions were made to improve the system. Was the organization just asking staff to try harder and to be more careful? Or were systemic changes being made?

Before learning PBCs, the executive might have been tempted to cherry-pick two data points in an attempt to prove that there was a 30% reduction. She might have created a slide that said:

Metric	Before	After	% Change
Falls	44 per week	26 per week (3/19/17)	-40.9%

That probably wouldn't convince a reader of this book.

She might have tried showing a linear trend line, which might convince some leaders, but not readers of this book.

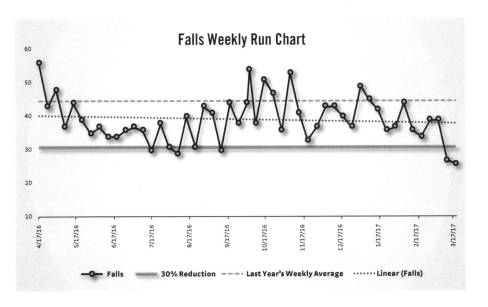

What does a Process Behavior Chart show? We see the following PBC Chart (the MR Chart, had no signals):

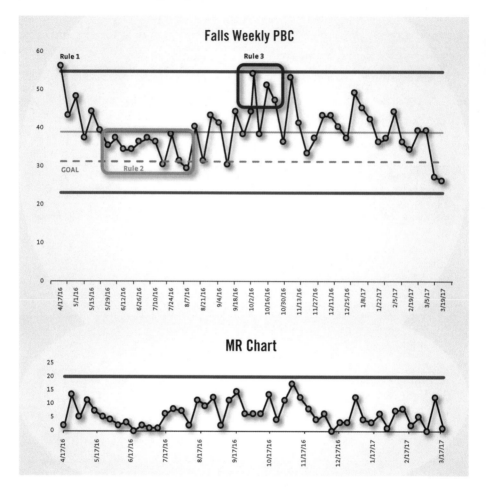

We see that the very first data point was above the Upper Limit *(Rule 1)*. After that, there was a run of 11 consecutive weeks below the average of 38.8 *(Rule 2)* that was calculated from the first 25 weeks of data. We also see a *Rule 3* signal. This is not a predictable system. What improvements could be made to make it predictable in a way that decreases the average number of falls?

It's clear something changed in the timeframe of the ***Rule 2*** signal. We might have hoped those 11 data points would be the start of a sustained shift downward in the number of falls. Instead of establishing a new average of around 34, the number of falls then increased and started to fluctuate around a higher number.

I asked the executive if she knew what happened during those 11 weeks; she had no answer. That improved performance had occurred almost a year earlier. If she went back to her organization and asked people closer to the point of care, they might have an answer, but it's tough after such a long time. If nobody knew or nobody would remember why falls were lower, we wouldn't want to pressure them into writing fiction as a response.

Was there some change made the week of May 29 that was then removed in August for some reason? If so, we'd want to consider reinstituting that change to see if falls then goes back down.

If this health system had been using a PBC instead of a Run Chart, they could have detected the signal immediately after the week of August 7 (the eighth consecutive point below the average). Leaders and the team could have worked to identify the cause of the signal. This could have been an example of using a PBC to discover an emergent improvement. The PBC tells us something changed. We don't know if it was an internal change that somebody initiated or if it was the result of an external factor.

We might presume that staff and managers were attempting improvements large and small. The PBC would tell us if anything had a significant impact.

If, after the signals, the system has again become predictable around the average of 38.8, the PBC allows that site to predict that, in future weeks, the number of falls would be between 22.8 and 54.8. This system is only rarely going to meet the target from management.

Asking why the number of falls was 53 one week likely wouldn't provide any more of a clear answer than asking why the number of falls was 27 some other week. Improving this system requires questions that are less reactive. Systematic analysis and improvements, as discussed in Chapter 4, could help them reduce the average. Ongoing use of the PBC would provide strong evidence of a downward shift to a lower average and, hopefully, less week-to-week variation.

Facility #2

We took the Run Chart for the second site and converted it to a PBC, using the first 25 points as the baseline period (which included data going back to February 2014).

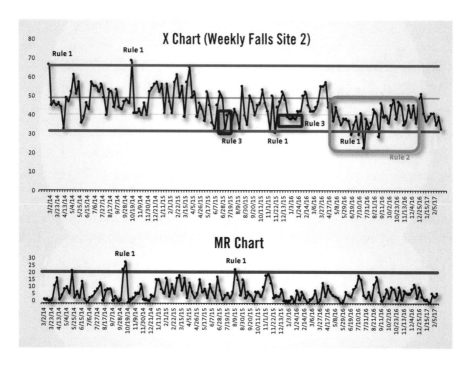

There are a few ***Rule 1*** signals in the X Chart (and corresponding signals in the MR Chart). Later, we see a ***Rule 2*** signal in the X Chart that suggests a downward shift in the average. Earlier, in June 2015, there are seven consecutive points below the average, but our rules tell us that is not a signal.

In this case, we can calculate a new average and new limits using the first 25 weeks that represent the new system that appeared to have started the week of April 17, 2016 (the first point below the initial average). Here is the PBC that shows that downward shift in performance:

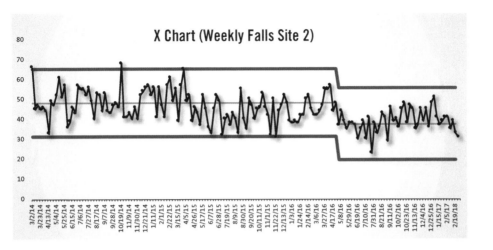

We now have a lower average (it fell from 49 to about 37.5). The limits are slightly wider in the X Chart since the Average Moving Range is slightly higher in the changed system), but the Upper and Lower Limits are both lower than before because they are evenly spread around the new, lower average.

Within this new system, we don't see any signals, which means we have a predictable system. In this new system, we can predict that the number of falls in a given week will be between the limits of 20 and 55.

The PBC allows us to say confidently that the average number of falls was reduced by 21% (the change in those two averages). This is not yet a 30% reduction, but it's more defensible than the claim of a 40% reduction that was based on cherry-picking two data points. However, they can be proud of the 20% reduction and keep improving on top of that.

It may cause some heartburn, however, if the organization doesn't know *why* falls have been reduced. If we've retroactively discovered this shift in the metric and we don't know what changed, there's a great risk that the system could change back to the way it was. If that happens, our performance might get worse.

Using the PBC each week going forward allows us to identify signals that show further improvement or degradation of performance. It also grounds us in the idea that improvement will be driven by asking how we can improve the system to reduce the average number of falls again.

Facility #3

Thankfully, the nursing executive didn't give up after our PBC analysis showed no improvement and 20% improvement in the first two facilities we examined.

Jumping right to the PBC for the third facility, we see ***Rule 2*** being triggered twice. It was almost one very long run below the old average other than the one data point that was above the baseline average. There were no signals in the MR Chart (not shown).

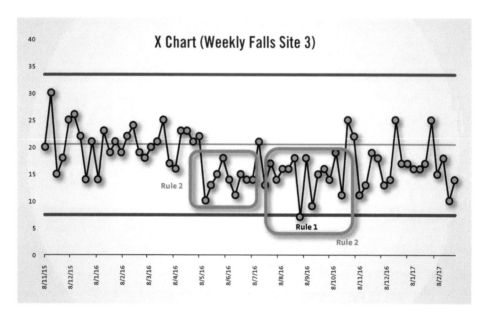

It appears that this facility has seen a downward shift in the number of falls. We can then create a revised X Chart that shows that shift:

Using the PBC each week allows us to identify signals that show further improvement or degradation of performance.

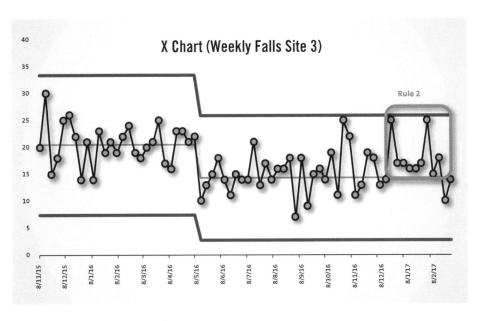

We see a reduction in the average from 20.5 to 14.4, which I would feel comfortable calling a 29.8% reduction in falls. Would you say that hits their organizational target of 30%? What matters more is understanding *why* there was a downward shift in the number of falls and what we can do to sustain that performance over time. Better yet, the organization would keep improving.

But, as you see boxed in red toward the end of the chart is a ***Rule 2*** signal, with nine consecutive weeks above the new average. Does the organization understand what caused this? The chart suggests that the average has crept up and that the number of falls is now going to fluctuate around an average of about 17.

Lessons for the Executive

The nurse executive walked away from our discussion a little disappointed that she couldn't prove that falls were reduced by 30%. She couldn't do so unless she resorted to the types of bad statistics that we discussed in Chapter 7 (such as two-data-point comparisons and linear trend lines). She was encouraged, however, that she had one facility that had managed to reduce falls by almost 30%. But her next job was to investigate why the number of falls at the second facility had gone back up.

In looking at her three charts, we discovered signals retroactively and then tried to understand the cause of the signal. If some best practices that were discovered in the third facility were going to be tried in either of the other two facilities, they would use the PBCs as a way of validating an intentional test of change by looking for a shift in the average, as we discussed in Chapter 4. Any of our three types of signals would indicate a significant change in the system, which could be the result of our intentional improvement efforts.

When Events Become Rare

As a hospital reduces falls (or when any organization reduces hopefully rare events like server crashes or defects reaching a manufacturing customer), the average number in a period might fall below one. In special cases like this, charting the number of rare incidents can be a bit problematic.

In the X Chart, below, since the average number of infections per week is just 0.13 and the Upper Limit is calculated to be 0.86, any week with one infection appears to be a signal. We could, in this case, investigate each infection's root cause.

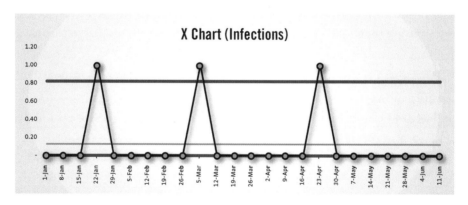

An X Chart with such a low average makes it difficult, however, to predict future performance or to tell if we are improving. We could look for eight consecutive weeks of zero infections (**_Rule 2_**). Or, we can instead plot the days between infections as a metric, where each data point is a particular incident. Such a chart would look like the one below, where we see that the days between infections is a predictable metric that is fluctuating around an average of 49.5 days. The last three data points show a **Rule 3** signal that would indicate that infections are becoming more frequent — therefore, we should investigate and try to correct whatever has changed in the system.

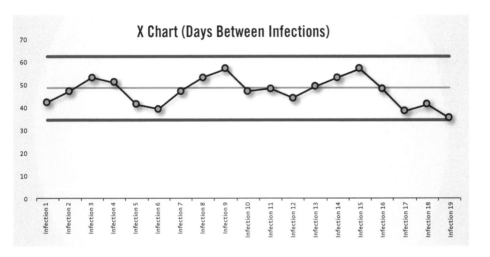

Hopefully, we could improve the system to further increase the average days between infections, using the PBC as a way of proving that we've improved.

Are Company Car Accidents Going Up?

I used to work for a healthcare consulting group where we were each given a company fleet vehicle to drive for work and personal use. Company data showed that the biggest risk of injury or death on the job was driving.

Thankfully, the company was concerned about our safety and took measures, including defensive driving courses and strict "no device use" policies (including talking hands-free). But, there were some problems with the way they measured and talked about safety over time. One year, we were given a presentation at a team meeting that said:

"Our current Accidents Per Million Miles (APMM) is at 4.58, well above our 2.80 target."

A simple comparison against a target doesn't tell us much. A target like 2.80 sounds like a textbook example of an arbitrary target. We know the answer to **Question 1**, but only for the current year. But, more important was **Question 2**, "Are we improving?"

What if the target had been 5.0? The safety performance would be better than the target, but we'd still want to improve. The ultimate goal for something safety related should be *zero* even if we're unlikely to ever achieve perfection. If there had been 2.75 APMM that year, would the corporate safe-driving specialist have been there talking to us? What was more important — hitting the target or continuously improving safety performance?

They showed us a chart that looked like this:

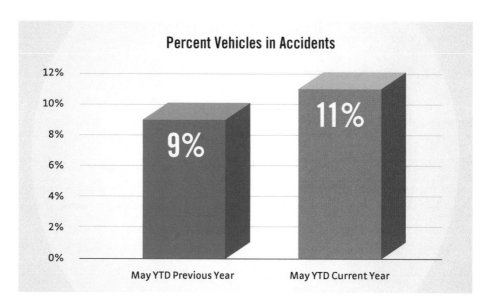

The only thing the chart tells us is that a higher percentage of cars were involved in accidents compared to the year before. It's a simplistic two-data-point comparison. There's nothing to indicate if this difference is signal or noise.

We could also nitpick about the use of a column chart for a time series chart, let alone the use of a 3D chart (which makes things harder to read). If the chart was clear to a reader, they wouldn't have to add the data point labels of 9% and 11%.

As we've learned in this book, the same system — the same drivers being just as careful driving the same cars — could result in more accidents some years than others.

A chart like this was then shown:

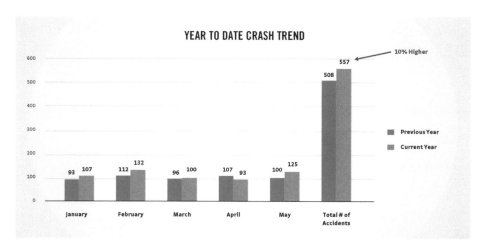

The year-to-date number showed 10% more accidents, as it was labeled. Again, it left me wondering if that increase was noise or signal.

I was able to get monthly data, as the team's representative on the safe-driving committee, so I drew a Run Chart, shown below:

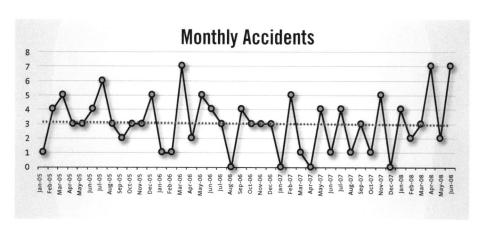

The addition of a linear trend line (in red) makes it look like the number of crashes is decreasing slightly over time. But, as discussed in Chapter 7, linear trend lines can be misleading.

Was our driving track record getting worse (as indicated by the slides presented to us) or was it getting better (as indicated by the linear trend line on my Run Chart)? Is it possible that both are true? Maybe neither is true. A PBC gives us a better method to answer **Question 2.**

What does the voice of the process tell us? We can try to answer this through the PBC below:

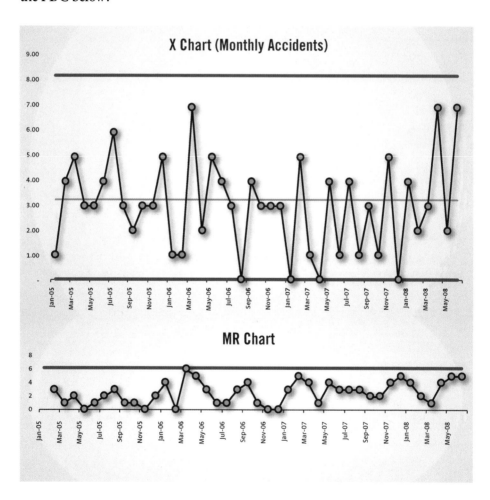

It's a predictable system. There are no signals. The PBC shows us the average number of accidents is 3.25 per month, and we can predict that any future month will bring between zero and eight accidents.

An executive might look at the chart and say, "Seven is too high! Why did we have seven accidents those months? That's the most ever." Being the highest number ever doesn't mean that it's a signal. The executive and the safe-driving committee should look for systemic improvements to the system. It's better to ask, "How can we reduce the average from 3.25 to, say, 1.5 accidents per month?" than it is to ask, "What went wrong that month?"

It also might not be very helpful to ask questions like "Why did we have zero accidents some months? Let's have everybody drive the way they did in those months!" It's possible that all of the company drivers were driving equally safely each month, but there are external factors (including other drivers) that cause more accidents in some months than others. The PBC method teaches us not to overreact to noise in the metric, whether it's good (zero accidents) or bad (seven or any above-average number).

What are some things the company could have done to improve the system? Maybe the company could hold safe-driving training once a year instead of every three years. What if the company stopped allowing employees to drive the company cars for personal use? That would reduce the number of miles driven and the number of accidents (but it probably wouldn't affect the Accidents Per Million Miles number), but employees would have been unhappy about losing a perk.

Lecturing the employees or showing us that the APMM number was above the target wasn't helpful. Could we all have been more careful? Maybe, but I generally wouldn't count on that as an improvement strategy.

As Wheeler writes:

> **"You need to live with this process, or start changing it. Looking for a root cause isn't going to do anything for you here. There's no assignable cause. Learn what your process is telling you."**

I tried bringing these points up in a constructive way, saying, "Let me show you how to look at the data in a better way." My manager politely told me to stop criticizing the safe-driving program. I wasn't criticizing the idea of the program. I was trying to propose a better way of looking at performance. I think that would have improved safety.

And so it goes. We'll discuss more about topics related to change management in Chapter 9. Having a technically correct approach doesn't guarantee acceptance or adoption of this new way.

CHAPTER 9

Getting Started With Process Behavior Charts

P rocess Behavior Chart methods have been around for decades without being widely adopted. Why?

After teaching a workshop on these methods, a student said to me, "These methods are correct, but it seems more difficult. But, it seems that the time spent setting up these charts would pay off in time you save down the road." He was struggling with the question of whether or not these methods would be accepted back at his organization.

Knowing a valid and helpful method, believing in the benefits of it, and trying to teach it to others can be challenging. Having a solution doesn't mean that others will accept it. One reason is that others might not realize (or accept) that a problem exists with their current methods. So, in their minds, there's no need for solutions.

"Show Me How To Do It"

Over the past 20 years, I've found myself in some situations where people were looking for a solution and for advice. I consulted for a hospital laboratory in a small Illinois community more than ten years ago. The lab director and her team were driven to improve, and they realized that meant working and managing in new ways.

In the context of a "Lean management system," the director asked me what their metrics and charts should look like. I proposed they use and post Run Charts for their daily metrics, which was a big improvement over their old monthly metrics report. They tracked five Key Performance Indicators (KPIs), such as the percentage of morning test results that were in patient records by 7 AM (a metric they chose) and their labor productivity metric (a metric that senior management mandated).

Leaders there insisted that the charts included green, yellow, and red zones for each metric, comparing them to a target and a "stretch goal." Part of me wishes I had pushed harder for the use of the full-blown Process Behavior Chart methodology, but sometimes baby steps are a good start. As they reviewed their Run Charts daily, it provided an opportunity for me to teach and coach them about not overreacting to noise in the metrics.

Over time, the director plotted each month's aggregate metric into a Run Chart. I then helped her look at those as PBCs, looking for sustained shifts in the metric, primarily through *Rule 2*. I wanted to see that they not only sustained their gains, but, better yet, continued improving using the Lean methods they learned and practiced.

One X Chart, below, shows two shifts upward in the 7 AM percentage:

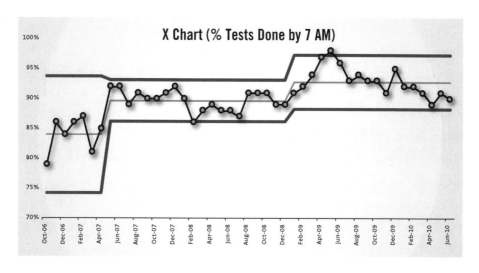

I remember discussions with a different hospital lab where they also asked for input on how to view their new daily metrics. I tried teaching the PBC approach but received what some call "pushback" on the idea. There were fears of it being too intimidating (an idea we could have tested instead of allowing the lab director to make that assumption). But, they used Run Charts instead of Bowling Charts, so that was progress.

Instead of blaming these labs for being resistant to PBCs, I looked in the mirror and asked what I could do to better explain how PBCs work and that they aren't that complicated. Or, maybe the root cause wasn't "poor explanation" and there were other factors involved. I should have started an A3 to help think through this problem — why weren't people embracing this better way (PBCs)? Why were they willing to accept a method (Run Charts) that's merely somewhat better?

I often think back to Wheeler's comments about PBCs being a way of thinking, with some tools attached. Even without the tools being used, I could teach the way of thinking. I emphasized that there are times when a metric fluctuates around an average. The same system sometimes generates different numbers. We shouldn't overreact to every below-average data point. It's better to have the thinking without the tools than it is to have the tools without the right thinking.

After our initial lab improvement and redesign project was done, I left and moved on to another client. But, within the year, the hospital invited me back to work with the radiology department. This gave me many opportunities to walk down the hall to visit the lab. One time, a medical technologist who had been part of their Lean project team said he wanted to talk about their metrics board.

He pointed up at their metrics and charts and said:

"When we have a day that's better than average, the lab leaders applaud and say things like 'nice job' and 'way to go.'

But, when we have a day that's worse than average, they say things like, 'It's OK, don't worry, it's the system.'

Isn't it *always* the system?"

He was understanding the way of thinking. If the chart didn't show any signals, it was always the system. Their system and their metric weren't statistically capable of meeting their target every single day, so that meant they needed to work on improving the system (as they were learning to do with Lean methods). His insightful question created an opportunity for me to coach his leaders in a way that the frontline employee didn't feel comfortable doing.

> It's better to have the thinking without the tools than
> it is to have the tools without the right thinking.

Walking back down the hall to radiology, we were still in the early stages of defining the problem statement for our project: Kids were waiting too long for outpatient MRI appointments.

Our key metric was the waiting time, measured in weeks. The starting point was 12 to 14 weeks, which was more than twice as long as the waiting time of the competing children's hospital in the area. Leaders (with the agreement of the team) set an aggressive target of a three-week waiting time. Prior to the project, the MRI area wasn't formally tracking the waiting time, and now they wanted to dramatically improve that number. A lower waiting time meant not only faster, better care for their patients. It also meant less stress and worry for parents, as an MRI often ruled out a very frightening diagnosis.

If appointment waiting time was a "results measure," then the MRI utilization percentage was a key "process measure." The project team realized, thankfully, that waiting times couldn't be reduced by rushing through their work (and they didn't want to jeopardize quality or safety). The team studied their existing system to look for causes of gaps in their daily schedules. Increasing utilization would mean more cases per day, which would result in shorter waiting times.

I did convince the project team and MRI manager to use a PBC to chart daily utilization rates. I taught them to look for signals and shifts in the metric, as shown in the figure below. Shifts were identified at points where *Rule 2* was triggered as the result of various improvements.

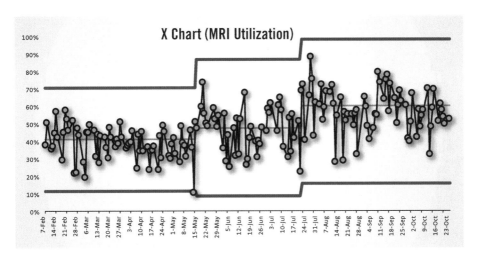

Over time, we saw multiple shifts upward, as the utilization rate for that MRI machine went from an average of 40% to an average of 48%, and then up again to an average of 60%. They learned that, unfortunately, not every day would reach 60%. The Natural Process Limits were very wide, meaning the team could work to reduce day-to-day variation in the system. Improving the system required systemic thinking, not reactive thinking.

As the team embraced Lean process redesign and management methods, the PBC approach quickly became accepted as the default way to track metrics in the MRI area. Over the course of one year, waiting times were gradually reduced to a range of two to three weeks, and that level of performance has been sustained for almost a decade.

"We Don't Have a Problem"

At one end of the spectrum is a client or an employer who says something like, "Just tell me how to manage my metrics, and I'll follow your recommendations." The other end of the spectrum includes people who think their current methods are just fine.

In the last chapter, I told the story about my suggestions for charting the safe-driving metrics and how my ideas seemed unwelcome. I recall another time, about 20 years ago when I still worked in manufacturing, when I was bombarded constantly with unhelpful (to me) comparisons of two data points.

Every time I logged into my computer at work, I was shown a "splash screen" with some key company goals and measures, all of which factored into the company multiplier portion of our annual bonus. One section of the screen included a Column Chart labeled "Customer Experience Metric Performance Summary." I'm not sure most employees knew what those words meant or how the four metrics were calculated (or what the acronyms meant). But, we were supposed to care and, I suppose, we were supposed to want to improve this score (and it was assumed we knew how to improve it).

The chart looked like this, where the Y axis was the percentage improvement over the current year:

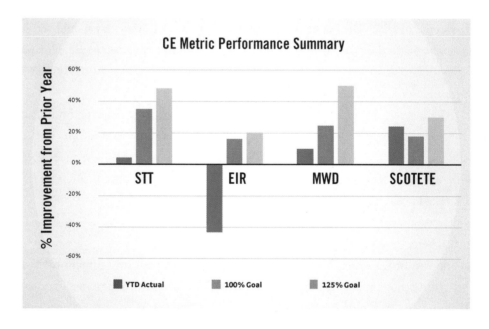

Three of the metrics were not improving as much as the target, and one metric's performance was worse than the year before. This chart showed two unhelpful comparisons: this year's number compared to last (the percent improvement) and this year's number compared to the target.

This somewhat answers **Question 1** (Are we achieving our target?) for the cumulative year-to-do metric. It somewhat answers **Question 2** (Are we improving?). But, both questions are answered only at the year-to-year level. We can't tell how performance is trending within the year. A Run Chart or a PBC with weekly or monthly data points would have been much more helpful.

If a metric is described as being "4% better than the previous year," you know by now to question that comparison. How do we know if a 4% difference represents signal or noise? If the 100% bonus target is set at a 35% improvement, does that threshold represent signal or noise? We don't know unless we plot the dots.

I thought I could help the company improve the way this data was presented. I re-read my copy of *Understanding Variation*. I spent a lot of time building an educational PowerPoint deck with 46 slides that illustrated how the current data-analysis methods that were shown to us on the various splash screens were inferior to PBCs.

Problems I saw in various settings within the company included:

- Declaring that a team had "improved" performance based on a Run Chart of five data points that was likely within the range of noise
- Showing long tables of monthly data points instead of Run Charts or PBCs
- Labeling a list of numbers with a positive "trend" when it appeared the metric was merely fluctuating
- Overreacting to and asking for an explanation for every up and down in a metric
- Not reacting to or learning from signals when they appeared, including shifts in the metric's average performance

I thought the recommendations in the slide deck were clear — use Run Charts (or better yet, PBCs) and the *Understanding Variation* way of thinking. I managed to schedule a presentation with a long-time employee who was fairly high up in the management chain. She patiently sat through the presentation, asked a few questions, and said that, while she learned a lot and it made sense, she didn't see the need to push for any changes.

Again, I felt like I'd failed. I had a method that was better, but it was completely cast aside. Looking back, I fault myself for pushing solutions (PBCs) before gaining agreement that there was a problem to begin with.

Accepting That Others Might not Accept Change

Over the course of my career, I've learned that change isn't always quickly accepted. People are complicated. It's important to acknowledge and respect that. We can't limit our thinking to exploring what the right answer should be. We also need to think about strategies that can engage others in the process of accepting change. Some people call this "change management." Effective change management doesn't involve telling people what to do or forcing people to change.

Some people are scared off by a method they think may be too difficult. The reality is that these methods can be used by frontline staff, managers, middle managers, executives, and board members.

Even if a method is technically sound, practical in use, and simple to understand, we still face a number of challenges in getting people to test the method. Pushing methods on others isn't necessarily effective or sustainable. Pushing change quite often leads to pushback — and that's understandable. Pushing back is human nature.

We need to work through that challenge instead of labeling others as "resistant to change" and implying they are bad people. Modern approaches to therapy and counseling, such as "motivational interviewing," teach us that resistance is a natural, normal, and expected phase in the process of an individual embracing a new way of doing things.

> Effective change management doesn't mean
> forcing people to do things a different way.

Before a new approach can be embraced, it helps if we can gain agreement that there is a problem with our current management methods. One challenge we face is that the question of adopting a new method is not purely a rational argument or discussion. The motivational interviewing (M.I.) method tells us that people tend to be "ambivalent" about change. Ambivalence means they might articulate reasons to change (called "change talk" in the M.I. language) while also stating reasons why they cannot change ("sustain talk"). "Ambivalence is a normal and natural part of the change process for human beings."[42]

In my work as a consultant, I've learned that, if you give advice when the recipient hasn't asked for it, that advice is likely to be ignored, no matter how correct it might be. The younger version of me, in engineer or consultant roles, would often bemoan the fact that somebody wasn't listening to me when I was right.

> "Ambivalence is a normal and natural part of
> the change process for human beings."

There is some risk in pointing out that there is a better way to manage because that implies we think there are problems with the old method — and people don't like to be told that they are wrong (and they don't like the softer language of "there are opportunities for improvement"). The pushback that we might face could be emotional as much as rational, and we need to respect and work through people's concerns.

I assume you're reading this book because you suspect there's a better way to manage and that we can be more effective with some new methods, even if you recognize that introducing change to an organization can be a bit scary. Your boss or your senior executives might think that they and their approach to management is fine. They might see the people who work for them as the problem. Some of your leaders might be quite comfortable with the status quo, as they're managing in ways they were taught, ways they developed, or "the way we've always done things around here," as people often say.

I've learned (often the hard way) that it's not enough to have the right answer if we can't get agreement that there is a problem and the need for a solution. I've stopped blaming others for not embracing new methods. We need to learn how to work with people in a more effective way. As they say, when you point a finger at someone else, there are three pointing back at you.

As it turns out, pushing back on unsolicited advice is human nature. That doesn't mean there's anything wrong with the person you're trying to help. It means they are, well, human.

A Helpful Change Management Model

Since good ideas or new approaches aren't guaranteed to be accepted by an organization, having an effective change management strategy can help. Sustainable change comes when it's truly accepted and embraced by the people in a organization.

The statistician George Box said, "Essentially, all models are wrong, but some are useful." I've found that it can be useful to have a change model to give us language and a framework about change that we use in a workplace. It's often said that change is not as easy as flipping a lightswitch; it's a process.

One useful model is known as the Prosci ADKAR® Model. Organizational transformation begins with individual change. The steps in this model are:

1. "Awareness of the need for change
2. Desire to support the change
3. Knowledge of how to change
4. Ability to demonstrate new skills and behaviors
5. Reinforcement to make change stick"[43]

As a reader, you still might be going through this change process. Hopefully, this book has helped build or strengthen your awareness of problems with existing methods for displaying and managing metrics and the need for change. You may have have approached it with a desire to support the adoption of Process Behavior Charts, or this book may have created or enhanced it. Knowledge about PBCs and the ability to then start creating or using them over time would, hopefully, be followed by reinforcement, which can probably only come through trying the PBC methodology and seeing for yourself if it's having the effect we might expect.

Change is not as easy as flipping a lightswitch; it's a process.

The Prosci ADKAR® Model is extended to four phases of organizational change adoption, which could very well apply to your initial use and rollout of PBCs.[44] It might be helpful to start small, using PBCs in one part of the business where early adopters can be properly trained, coached, and mentored instead of trying to implement everywhere all at once. The four phases are:

1. Business need: What is the impact of the unresolved gaps in your key metrics? How much time is wasted by overreacting to noise and searching for root causes that don't exist? How much can be gained by using PBCs?

2. Concept and design: What is your plan for starting to use PBCs? How will you train others and do an initial test of these methods? What technology will you use?

3. Implementation: How will you get started and evaluate what is working well, what is not, and what the organizational benefits appear to be?

4. Post-implementation: What is your evaluation of your pilot program? How will you spread these methods to other areas? What is your plan for reinforcing, sustaining, and improving your approach to PBCs over time?

One final model that I have found to be helpful for thinking through, planning, and executing organizational change is the ExperiencePoint change model. The seven-step model is an adaptation of Dr. John Kotter's "8-step process for leading change."[45]

The ExperiencePoint model has seven steps. Phase 1, including the first three steps, focuses on developing a solution by aligning key stakeholders. This is followed by Phase 2, which then engages the organization in implementing and sustaining the change.[46]

Phase 1:

1. **Understand** the current condition, the need for change, and the business case and rationale for using PBCs (the why).
2. **Enlist** an initial core team of diverse stakeholders to work on the initiative (the who).
3. **Envisage** a future state where PBCs are used and the implications for the broader organization.

Phase 2:

4. **Motivate** others in the organization by sharing the challenge, solution, and vision with them (back to the why, but more broadly).
5. **Communicate** the vision for using PBCs, and develop the final plan for testing the methodology.
6. **Act** by taking steps to test the use of PBCs, while also aligning people, processes, and technologies with this new approach.
7. **Consolidate** the change by reinforcing and spreading what is working with PBCs and improving the things that can be better.

In the Kotter model, the first step is to "create a sense of urgency." In the ExperiencePoint model, we help the broader organization "see the need for change through a bold, aspirational statement that communicates the importance of acting immediately" only after an initial vision for change has been created. Otherwise, there is a risk that creating the proverbial "burning platform" will only increase anxiety and fear if it's not possible to act quickly. That's why the Phase 1 guiding coalition works through the first three steps to create the vision that can then be taken to the rest of the organization.

As you think about how to start using PBCs in your workplace, think about these change models. It's important to know *what* to do; it's also necessary to think about *how* we go about it.

Call to Action

I would love to hear from you as you adopt Process Behavior Charts in your workplace. What works well? What questions do you have? You can contact me via email at mark@markgraban.com. Feel free to share your PBCs with me, and let me know what you have learned from them and how they have helped you save time and improve more.

For further learning, you can see links and more resources online at the book's website, www.MeasuresOfSuccessBook.com.

I'm curious to hear how you use the tools. I'm also interested in how you have adopted and spread the PBC way of thinking. Do you and your leaders no longer react to noise in a metric? Are you using PBCs and our three rules as a way to show a significant and sustained improvement instead of using two data points or a linear trend line? Can you better answer our three core questions?

If you have case studies of organizational success stories about adopting this methodology, I'd love to hear about them. Perhaps they can be shared on my blog (www.LeanBlog.org) or in an updated edition of this book. Thanks for reading!

APPENDIX A

How to Create Process Behavior Charts

Most of this book is focused on using and interpreting Process Behavior Charts (PBCs). Most leaders are probably going to be in a position of reading and interpreting PBCs. Here, we'll learn how to create PBCs and will get more practice in learning from the charts and using them for improvement.

Generally, people will use software to create their PBCs and to perform the underlying calculations. It's possible to create PBCs by hand, but most of us have spreadsheet software available. In some circumstances, we might create a PBC electronically and then have a team add daily or weekly data points onto the chart by hand until the next time the chart is updated electronically.

In my experience, Microsoft Excel works well for creating PBCs. You can usually export data from a system into Excel to work on it from there. This gives you a great deal of control over the data points that you use for the baseline and you can adjust the formatting of charts to your liking. There's also a risk that incorrect formulas might work their way into spreadsheets as this method spreads through an organization. For example, we want to ensure people use the correct formulas for calculating Natural Process Limits instead of setting the limits manually or confusing them with targets.

You can download a free Excel file or a Google Sheet that I've created with the formulas and the charts built in, ready for you to input data. See links and more resources online at www.MeasuresOfSuccessBook.com/resources.

There are also many specialized software systems and reporting tools that will create different forms of Control Charts. But, be careful about the methodology that's embedded in the software. Make sure that the software allows you to use the correct form of chart (the X and MR Charts), that it uses the correct method for calculating limits, and that it doesn't overwhelm you with additional rules for signals. As introduced earlier, the methodology of this book recommends three rules for the X Chart and one for the MR Chart.

1) Get the Initial Baseline Data

In this appendix, we'll create a PBC from scratch, building upon a blank spreadsheet. I've found that it's a helpful exercise for people who are new to PBCs to go through this process at least once, to better internalize the formulas and the approach. But, over time, you'd likely use a template file as a starting point.

In most cases, unless we are starting with a brand-new metric, we have historical data available to create our initial PBC. This initial chart takes a retrospective look back at recent system performance to see if the system is predictable. Ideally, we'd have 20 historical data points available for calculating the initial average and Natural Process Limits.

There are diminishing returns, in terms of the validity of the limits, from using additional data points for the baseline. The limits, as calculated, are intended to filter out about 99% of all noise. There is always a risk of a missed signal or a false signal, based on the probabilistic nature of the limits, but the methodology is designed to balance out those risks.

Using 25 baseline data points is only marginally better than having 20, in terms of accuracy and validity. Some references say to use 25 data points if you have them; sometimes, I use 24 since that represents two years of monthly data. The exact number of baseline data points used is not critically important, since the average and limits won't be that different usually as the result of using more or fewer data points. The validity of the limits will be about the same. You can experiment with your spreadsheet to see what happens when you choose different baseline timeframes for your PBC. What's important is that we create PBCs and use them appropriately over time — the thinking more so than the tool.

If necessary, you can create a PBC with just six or eight data points if that's all you have to start with. The only caveat is that the limits won't be as valid, statistically, as if you had 20 baseline data points or more. But, starting with a small number of data points is better than managing by the red/green approach or two-data-point comparisons. Again, a PBC becomes more valid as you add baseline data points. In a situation like this, you can recalculate the average and limits as you add data, up until the point of having those initial 20 data points.

Once you then get to 20 data points, it's important to *not* continually recalculate the Natural Process Limits as new data points are added over time. The average and limits should *not* be continually recalculated based on the 20 most recent data points, for example. In using the PBC over time, we keep the average and the limits the same until we reach a point when we see a clear signal of a shift in the system, the data, and the chart.

Rational Subgroups

It's important to make sure (or at least have a solid assumption) that the historical data is part of the same system. When plotting my daily LeanBlog.org traffic on a PBC, I could choose to chart only weekdays, since I know traffic is lower on weekends. I could consider weekends and holidays to be a different system. Or, I could plot the data on a weekly basis, which removes that weekend effect from the chart (but also means a slower detection of signals).

If a factory is looking at production on a per-shift basis, the day shift and night shift might each form their own rational subgroup. This would be especially true if staffing levels and planned production are lower on the night shift, meaning we would expect a lower average production at night. Instead of a single PBC that would show a continual up-down-up-down pattern, we should instead create two separate PBCs for each shift.

We shouldn't be arbitrarily choosing timeframes for PBCs that tell the story we want to tell. We should be using the PBCs in a way that helps us best answer our three core questions (except I don't have a target here, so I can answer only *Question 2* and *Question 3*).

2) Calculate the Central Line for the X Chart

The central line in our X Chart is generally the mean of our data. There are some instances when it makes sense to use the median, but we typically use the mean, which is often called the "average."

Technically speaking, what we normally call the "average" is called the "arithmetic mean." The median of a data set (the point where half the data is higher and half the data is lower), is another form of "average." The mean and median are, in effect, two different types of average. In this book, we'll do like typical spreadsheet software does, and use the term "average" and "arithmetic mean" interchangeably, since that's the common usage.

Calculating the average of our baseline data points is straightforward. The Excel formula in cell C2 would simply be =AVERAGE(B2:B26) if we are using 25 data points. We set cell C3 with the formula =C2 and then copy that formula down so that the average is the same through the data set. The average will remain the same until we possibly see a shift in the system based on the PBC evaluation rules.

It can be helpful to shade in the cells that are used for the baseline to provide a visual reference that doesn't require looking at the formula in cell C2. This becomes more helpful once we've added more data points over time. The spreadsheet might now look like this:

	A	B	C
1		Data	Average
2	4/10/16	44	39.36
3	4/17/16	38	39.36
4	4/24/16	43	39.36
5	5/1/16	48	39.36
6	5/8/16	37	39.36
7	5/15/16	44	39.36
8	5/22/16	39	39.36
9	5/29/16	35	39.36
10	6/5/16	37	39.36
11	6/12/16	34	39.36
12	6/19/16	45	39.36
13	6/26/16	36	39.36
14	7/3/16	37	39.36
15	7/10/16	36	39.36
16	7/17/16	30	39.36
17	7/24/16	43	39.36
18	7/31/16	31	39.36
19	8/7/16	41	39.36
20	8/14/16	40	39.36
21	8/21/16	50	39.36
22	8/28/16	43	39.36
23	9/4/16	41	39.36
24	9/11/16	30	39.36
25	9/18/16	44	39.36
26	9/25/16	38	39.36

3) Draw a Run Chart

We then create a simple Run Chart with two lines: the data and the average. In Excel, this is called a "Line Chart," and it can be created with just a few clicks. The chart below shows the data, in blue, and the average as a horizontal line, in green.

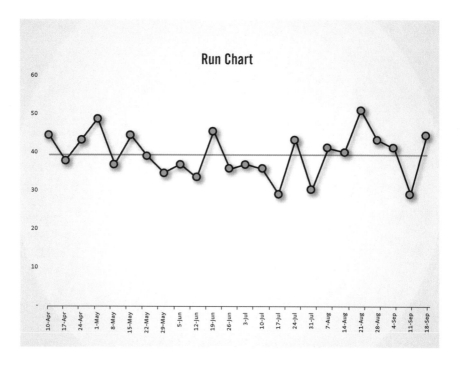

If this turns out to be a predictable system with fluctuating performance over time, we'd expect to see about half of the data points be above the average and half to be below the average. That is often the case. However, that isn't necessarily *always* going to be true, since the PBC methodology does not require data to be normally distributed (think a "bell curve").[47] It's possible we could have a predictable system with, for example, 70% of points being above or below the average.

As Wheeler teaches, the PBC approach is robust and works with many statistical distributions. This simplifies our efforts, as we don't have to analyze the distribution or transform the data in any way. That makes the PBC method very reasonable and practical for everyday management use.

A Run Chart can be helpful in that we can take an initial look to see if there is a trend of any eight consecutive data points on the same side of the average (***Rule 2***). The chart above appears like it is a predictable process. But, we need to calculate the Upper and Lower Natural Process Limits to know for certain if we only have noise in the chart by being able to also use **Rule 1** and **Rule 3**.

Some people in your organization might balk at the idea of the full-blown PBC methodology. If that's the case, starting with Run Charts can serve as baby steps to get people started with looking at a visualization of their metrics, weaning them off of Bowling Charts or other such text-based methods.

You might notice that we haven't talked yet about a target for this data. Again, a target or goal might count as the "voice of the customer" (or it's merely the "voice of management," as Wheeler says).

4) Calculate the Moving Ranges and the Average Moving Range

Unlike some Control Chart or Statistical Process Control methodologies where you would calculate a standard deviation from your data, the PBC method instead expresses the routine variation based on what's called the "Moving Ranges," as we introduced initially in Chapter 2.

A Moving Range (MR) is the absolute value of the difference between each two consecutive data points on the X Chart. The MR for the second data point is the absolute value of the second data point minus the first. The first data point doesn't have an MR because there's no previous data point to which it can be compared.

In Excel, we would enter the formula =ABS(B3-B2) into cell D3. We can copy and paste that formula down the column so that each data point from the second one on has an MR.

It's very important to note that if you forget the "ABS" and enter =(B3-B2) as the formula, you'll end up with some negative numbers for the MRs, which will throw off the calculation of your limits. We should also never see negative values in the MR Chart. It's helpful to do a visual check and confirm that you never see a negative number in the MR column (or use the Lean concept of "error proofing" to use conditional formatting to highlight any negative value that might appear).

If we based the initial average on the first 25 data points, we then calculate the Average Moving Range (or "MR-bar") for the first 24 Moving Ranges. We enter the formula =AVERAGE(D3:D26) in cell E2. The MR-bar in this example is calculated as 6.75.

	A	B	C	D	E
1		Data	Average	Moving Range (MR)	MR Bar
2	4/10/16	44	39.36		6.75
3	4/17/16	38	39.36	6	6.75
4	4/24/16	43	39.36	5	6.75
5	5/1/16	48	39.36	5	6.75
6	5/8/16	37	39.36	11	6.75
7	5/15/16	44	39.36	7	6.75
8	5/22/16	39	39.36	5	6.75
9	5/29/16	35	39.36	4	6.75
10	6/5/16	37	39.36	2	6.75
11	6/12/16	34	39.36	3	6.75
12	6/19/16	45	39.36	11	6.75
13	6/26/16	36	39.36	9	6.75
14	7/3/16	37	39.36	1	6.75
15	7/10/16	36	39.36	1	6.75
16	7/17/16	30	39.36	6	6.75
17	7/24/16	43	39.36	13	6.75
18	7/31/16	31	39.36	12	6.75
19	8/7/16	41	39.36	10	6.75
20	8/14/16	40	39.36	1	6.75
21	8/21/16	50	39.36	10	6.75
22	8/28/16	43	39.36	7	6.75
23	9/4/16	41	39.36	2	6.75
24	9/11/16	30	39.36	11	6.75
25	9/18/16	44	39.36	14	6.75
26	9/25/16	38	39.36	6	6.75

5) Calculate the Natural Process Limits

Now, we can add the Upper and Lower Natural Process Limits to what is now becoming the X Chart. Again, the limits on these charts are calculated from our baseline data; they are the voice of the process. We do not get to choose the limits.

The PBC limits are calculated in a way that balances out the risk of two different mistakes:

- Missing a signal of a change to the system
- Thinking there is a signal when there was no change to the system

The PBC limits will include approximately 99% to 100% of routine variation, which filters out most of our noise in the metric.[48]

Some Control Chart methodologies use a calculated standard deviation, or a "sigma" value and would describe "plus and minus 3-sigma limits" that are three standard deviations above and below the average. In the PBC methodology, we use a different method and formula to approximate what are essentially the plus and minus 3-sigma limits.

We use the Average Moving Range as a way of expressing routine variation, with the advantage, again, that our data set does not have to be normally distributed for this to be valid.

The PBC limits are calculated as:

Lower Natural Process Limit = Average − 3 * (MR-bar) / 1.128

Upper Natural Process Limit = Average + 3 * (MR-bar) / 1.128

We multiply by three (for the approximation of three sigma) but then have to divide by 1.128, a statistical factor based on some detailed probability rules that aren't very relevant to the typical user of Process Behavior Charts. You can find deeper-dive articles and book chapters by Wheeler on this subject, who developed this method.[49]

Other Control Chart methods also have rules for finding signals that are based on the narrower 1-sigma or 2-sigma limits, but Wheeler's PBC method does not use those rules. Therefore, we don't have to calculate, draw, or worry about those limits, especially since using those additional rules increases the risk of false signals and complicates the method.

As an alternative, you can also use the simpler PBC formulas of:

Natural Process Limit = Average +/− 2.66 * (MR-bar)

The Excel formula for the Lower Limit is:

$$= C2 - 3 * E2 / 1.128 \text{ or } = C2 - 2.66 * E2$$

And the Upper Limit formula is:

$$= C2 + 3 * E2 / 1.128 \text{ or } = C2 + 2.66 * E2$$

This gives us a Lower Limit of 21.41 and an Upper Limit of 57.31.

With these limits, if we have a predictable system, the PBC predicts that our future data points would most likely fall between 21.41 and 57.31 — unless something changes in the system.

In Excel, the formulas might look like this:

	A	B	C	D	E	F	G
1	Week of	Data	Average	Moving Range (MR)	MR Bar	Lower Limit	Upper Limit
2	42470	44	=AVERAGE(B2:B26)		=AVERAGE(D3:D26)	=C2-3*E2/1.128	=C2+3*E2/1.128
3	=A2+7	38	=C2	=ABS(B3-B2)	=E2	=F2	=G2
4	=A3+7	43	=C3	=ABS(B4-B3)	=E3	=F3	=G3
5	=A4+7	48	=C4	=ABS(B5-B4)	=E4	=F4	=G4
6	=A5+7	37	=C5	=ABS(B6-B5)	=E5	=F5	=G5

There are times when we might need to manually set the Lower or Upper Limit:

- If the X Chart is a metric that cannot be negative (such as something that is counted), then the Lower Limit should be set to zero.
- If the X Chart is a metric where 100% is the highest possible value (such as an on-time delivery percentage), then the Upper Limit should be set to 100%.

6) Create and Review the Initial X Chart

Adding the limits as new lines on the Run Chart turns it into an X Chart, as we see below:

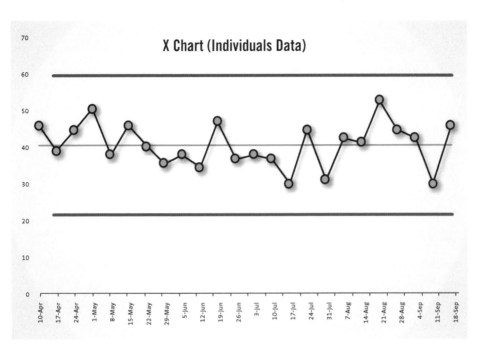

Do we see any signals in the chart? The three rules we use to identify signals in the X Chart of a PBC are:

- **Rule 1**: Any data point outside of the limits.
- **Rule 2**: Eight consecutive points on the same side of the central line.
- **Rule 3**: Three out of four consecutive data points that are closer to the same limit than they are to the central line.

Some sources will list additional rules for finding signals, such as the "Western Electric Rules," "Shewhart Rules," or "Nelson Rules." Adding more rules increases the risk of "false positive" signals, so we can follow Wheeler's advice to use just these three rules.[50]

There is an additional single rule we use to identify signals in the MR Chart:

- **Rule 1**: Any data point above the Upper Range Limit

It's easiest to see that there are no points outside of the limits (**Rule 1**). Additionally, there aren't any runs of eight consecutive points above or below the average (**Rule 2**). We also don't see three out of four consecutive points that are closer to a limit than they are to the central line (**Rule 3**).

The chart looks like the varying output of a predictable system. We might not like the level of performance, but we have a predictable metric, which means we can predict future performance and we have a stable foundation for our systematic improvement work, as we discussed in Chapter 4.

The data used for this example is the number of falls in a large hospital. In this healthcare context, it makes sense that if the same people are doing the same work (providing the same care) to the same types of patients, that the number of falls would be a function of that system.

Some weeks, the number is higher, and, some weeks, it's lower. Again, we can predict that, in upcoming weeks, the number of falls is mostly likely to be between 22 and 57 falls, unless we improve the system or something changes significantly in the system to affect performance.

Sometimes, the initial X Chart will not present itself as a predictable system, as seen in this next chart:

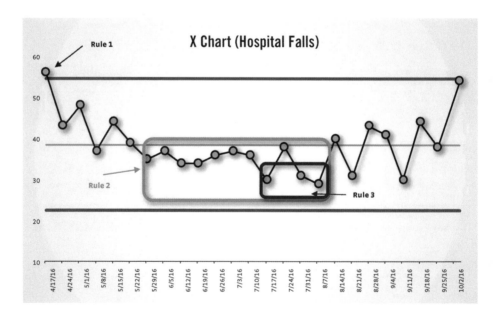

The signals in this chart are:

- The first data point is above the Upper Limit *(Rule 1)*
- A run of 11 consecutive points below the baseline average *(Rule 2)*
- Having 3 of 4 consecutive data points that are closer to the Lower Limit than they are to the average (*Rule 3*)

If we create an initial chart with some signals in the baseline time period, we do not have to exclude the data points that are signals from our calculated average and limits. It's more helpful to recognize that we have signals and to try to understand the special causes that are behind them. Then, as we track the metric over time and add data points to the chart, we can see if our system has become predictable (as the result of our problem solving or external factors) or if we still see an unpredictable system (if we have done nothing or tried changes that didn't affect our metric).

From this historical data and our calculated limits, we cannot confidently predict the future number of falls in the last scenario. One thing worth investigating would be asking why the number of falls was slightly lower from 5/29/16 to 8/7/16 when we saw that *Rule 2* signal. Were there fewer patients seen over the summer? It might be helpful, in this case, to look at a "per capita" metric of falls per patient-day. We might also want to look at monthly data for a longer time period to see if there is seasonality.

Leaders of this system can still, of course, ask systemic questions about improvement in an effort to reduce the number of falls below the average of 38.6. Our aim isn't just to have a predictable system; it's improvement and bringing that average down closer to zero.

Again, when working to improve a system, there are two different questions to ask (and two different paths to improvement, as discussed in Chapter 4):

1. How do we eliminate and prevent the recurrence of special causes that lead to negative signals in our metric? Or, if we see a positive signal, can we understand what changed and how to lock that in so we establish a new predictable system that performs better?

2. If we see nothing but noise in the data, can we systematically improve the system in a way that improves average performance? Can we also or instead reduce variation, depending on what's important in the situation?

7) Create and Review the MR Chart

Again, the full and complete PBC methodology includes two charts that are linked together:

1. The chart of the actual data points (sometimes called the "X Chart" or the "Individuals Chart")
2. The chart of the Moving Ranges (called the "MR Chart")

The intent of the MR Chart is to help us see if the amount of period-to-period variation is consistent over time. There are times when the X Chart data points will appear to be all noise, but seeing a data point above the MR Chart's Upper Range Limit signifies a change in the amount of underlying variation. This provides an additional signal that something has changed in the system, something we should react to and investigate even though the change hasn't yet affected our metric as plotted on the X Chart.

Creating the MR Chart is easy. We first plot the "MR" data points. Since the MR values are never negative, this chart has only an Upper Range Limit, which is calculated using a statistical constant of 3.268 times the MR-bar value.

MR Upper Range Limit = MR Bar * 3.268 or

= E2 * 3.268

Going back to our original example from this chapter, the Upper Limit for the MR Chart is 22.07.

	A	B	C	D	E	F	G	H
1		Data	Average	Moving Range (MR)	MR Bar	Lower Limit	Upper Limit	MR Upper Limit
2	4/10/16	44	39.36		6.75	21.41	57.32	22.07

We add that as a horizontal line on our MR Chart, displaying it with the paired X Chart:

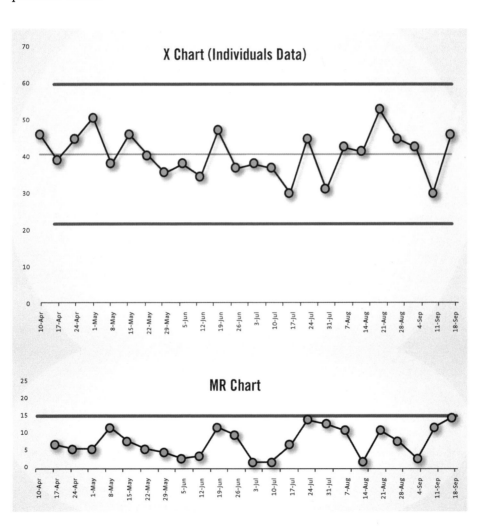

We use one rule in evaluating the MR Chart to look for signals:

- Are there any points above the Upper Range Limit? *(Rule 1)*

This MR Chart tells us that a change between any two data points in our metric that's greater than 22 is a signal that something changed in our system. Each data point above the Upper Range Limit should prompt us to investigate and see if we can determine what changed.

We saw *Rule 1* being triggered in the MR Chart of one of our PBCs for Tier 1 leads in Chapter 3. If we were using only the X Chart, we'd want to continually look for very large jumps in the chart that are unusual, such as going from near the Lower Limit to near the Upper Limit, as shown below:

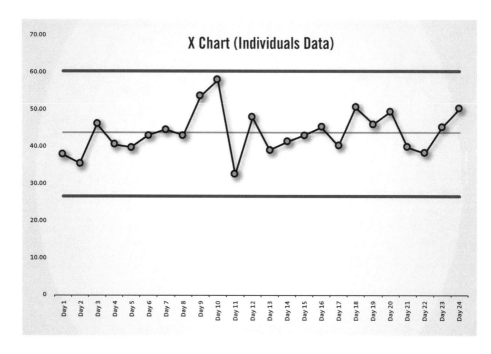

The large decrease from Day 10 to Day 11 is not a signal on the X Chart. Even without drawing an MR Chart, that large decrease should jump out at us. Or, it will over time as you get more experience with PBCs and build some intuition.

Using both charts together is technically correct, but, in practice, many organizations that use this methodology use just the X Chart that shows the actual data. This simplifies the method and is less likely to confuse the uninitiated, but there is a small chance that we miss some signals that would be identified only by the MR Chart. And, missing signals means missing opportunities for improvement.

My recommendation is to start off using both the X and MR Charts, looking to build intuition about what to look for over time. If your organization balks at using two charts for each metric, saying it might confuse people, you might use only the X Chart. Of course, another reaction to people being confused by the MR Chart might be to provide more (or better) training and coaching on the methodology.

Oh, and here is the MR Chart that was missing from the last example:

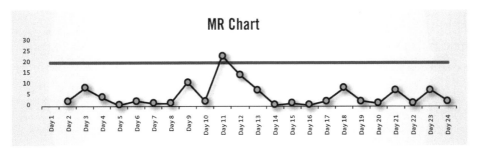

We can see, for Day 11, that the MR value is above the Upper Range Limit, as we might have intuited from the X Chart. The advantage of using the MR Chart is that we don't have to guess if there is a **Rule 1** signal or not.

8) Add Data Points Over Time, Look for Signals, Continue to Improve

The main purpose of the Process Behavior Chart is to help us improve. The PBC helps us save time by not reacting to noise in the metric. We can then reserve time and energy for investigating signals, which is a good use of time.

Alternatively, we can use the PBC to help prove or disprove that the system's performance has improved significantly or sustainably after we've made a change.

When our performance is not meeting our targets, we should still choose, in the absence of signals, to work on improving the system in a way that improves the average. We might also see a signal that is not the result of our improvement work, which is all the more reason to investigate and learn what has changed in our system.

As time goes on, we add more data points to the chart. As time progresses, you might choose to show the most recent 30 or 50 data points on the chart, allowing older data points to fall off the chart as time progresses (without deleting the underlying data). As we add more data points, we look for signals using our rules.

Throughout the book, you see examples of shifts in a metric that lead us to calculate a new average and new limits that reflect the fact that the system has changed.

9) Shift the Limits, When Appropriate

There are times when it's appropriate to shift the average and the limits to reflect a changed system that is performing differently than it was previously. The most likely signal that reflects a sustained shift in performance is seeing eight or more consecutive data points that are above or below the previous average (*Rule 2*).

Using our first example from this chapter, a metric that counts the number of patient falls, we might see a situation where a team has started testing an improvement that they expect will reduce falls. They have formed a hypothesis that says having patients wear bright yellow socks if they are at a high risk for falls will reduce falls. This would happen because staff will have a better visual if they see a high-risk patient walking without assistance, allowing them to more quickly intervene and help.

After the intervention, we see eight consecutive points below the baseline average (*Rule 2*). This suggests that our hypothesis is true that the yellow socks helped reduce falls in a sustained way. There is, of course, a risk that some *other* change to the system is what made the difference. A PBC will tell us that *something* has changed; it won't necessarily tell us *what* changed.

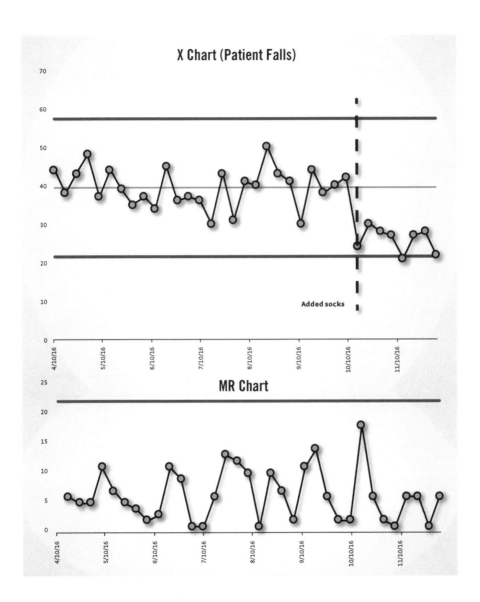

We could calculate a new average and limits from the eight points that represent the newly changed system. However, we should keep in mind that the limits won't be as valid, statistically, as the initial limits that were based on 25 data points.

The new average and new limits from those eight data points are:

- Average = 25.9
- Lower Limit = 15.2
- Upper Limit = 36.5
- MR Upper Limit = 13.1

The chart with the newly shifted limits would look like this:

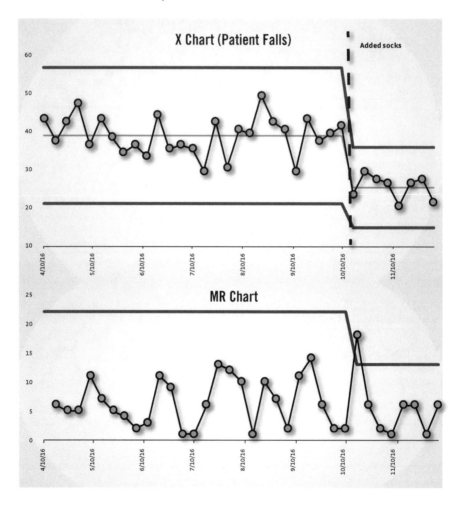

The PBC tells us we have a new system that's predictable around a new, lower, average. We could somewhat confidently predict that the next weeks would have been within the limits, or between 16 and 36 falls. Our prediction is not quite as confident as before because our new average and limits are currently calculated with just eight data points.

When we've made an improvement, as seen above, the PBC helps us see that we shouldn't overreact if number of falls went up from 24 to 30 falls in a single week, just because it's above the new average. Being above the current average once is not a signal. We don't want to fall back into the old habit of asking why one week was worse than the previous because two data points usually don't make a trend unless we see a *Rule 1* signal in the X or MR Charts.

However, a single week above the new Upper Limit of 36.5 (*Rule 1*) would suggest that the system has degraded or that some new problem has occurred. We would have to investigate to see if, for example, the yellow socks were no longer being used for some reason. It's important to ask *why* instead of just criticizing the worsened performance. For example, it's possible that the department ran out of yellow socks. If so, that could lead us to a different countermeasure, such as improving the inventory management system. Improving the system is more effective than the old habit of assuming problems are due to bad people not following the new process.

If we decide an average of nearly 26 falls per week is still too high, our team might then try another intervention that leads to a prediction or a hypothesis of improvement — looking for another signal that shows the system has improved.

Creating Your First Process Behavior Chart

If you haven't already been inspired to do so, please take a few minutes to create your first PBC. You can build a spreadsheet from scratch using the instructions above, or you can start with this Excel spreadsheet or Google Sheet.

You can use data that you have available in the workplace. You could find data online, such as the total annual rainfall numbers for your city. Or, you can start tracking data that you can collect in your life, such as your daily time to commute from home to work (your door to desk time, the driving time, etc.).

I'd love it if you'd share your example with me via email (Mark@MarkGraban. com) or you can post it on social media, tag me, and add the hashtag #plotthedots.

Single Page Summary: Process Behavior Charts

1. **Get the Initial Baseline Data**
   a. Ideally, have 20 data points as a baseline
   b. Can start with just six data points, worst case
2. **Calculate the Central Line for the X Chart**
   a. The average of the baseline data points
3. **Draw a Run Chart**
   a. Plot the data points
   b. Add a horizontal line for the average
4. **Calculate the Moving Ranges (MRs) and Average Moving Range**
   a. Each data point from the second one on has an MR value
   b. MR [Point 2] = Absolute value of [Point 2 minus Point 1]
5. **Calculate the Natural Process Limits**
   a. Lower Natural Process Limit = Average – 2.66 * (MR-bar)
   b. Upper Natural Process Limit = Average + 2.66 * (MR-bar)
6. **Create and Review the X Chart**
   a. Add the Upper and Lower Limits to the X Chart
   b. Look for signals:
      - *Rule 1:* Any data point outside of the limits.
      - *Rule 2:* Eight consecutive points on the same side of the central line.
      - *Rule 3:* Three out of four consecutive data points that are closer to the same limit than they are to the central line.
7. **Create and Review the MR Chart**
   a. Calculate the Upper Range Limit = Average MR * 3.268
   b. Plot the MR points, and add the MR Upper Range Limit to the chart
   c. Look for signals (Rule 1 only)
8. **Add Data Points Over Time, Look for Signals, Continue to Improve**
   a. Do not continually recalculate the average or the limits
9. **Shift the Limits, When Appropriate**

APPENDIX B

Summary of Key Points

KEY POINT #1: We don't manage the metric; we manage the system that leads to the results, and we lead the people who help us improve the system.

KEY POINT #2: Two data points are not a trend.

KEY POINT #3: "No data have meaning apart from their context."

KEY POINT #4: A chart will always tell us more than a list of numbers.

KEY POINT #5: The job of management is not just to look backward but also to look forward and predict, if possible, what is likely to occur.

KEY POINT #6: There is variation in every metric or data set. Process Behavior Charts filter out noise so we can identify signals.

KEY POINT #7: Don't waste time explaining noise in a metric. There is no simple, single "root cause" for noise.

KEY POINT #8: More timely data is better for improvement. Daily is better than weekly, which is better than monthly, as long as we don't overreact to every data point.

KEY POINT #9: If there was an intervention in the system, make it clear in your chart or your discussion of the chart when that change was started or implemented.

KEY POINT #10: When showing the "before" scenario, show enough data points to illustrate the previous level of variation, not just a single data point.

APPENDIX C

Additional Resources

For more information, including downloadable templates, blog posts, and additional examples that will be updated over time, please visit the resources page for this book:

https://www.measuresofsuccessbook.com/resources/

Additional Reading

Core books:

- *Understanding Variation: The Key to Managing Chaos* (Wheeler)
- *Out of the Crisis* (Deming)
- *The New Economics* (Deming)
- *Four Days with Dr. Deming* (Latzko and Saunders)
- *Fourth Generation Management* (Joiner)

Reading on goals, targets, and strategy:

- *The Balanced Scorecard: Translating Strategy into Action* (Kaplan and Norton)
- *Getting the Right Things Done* (Dennis)
- *Hoshin Kanri for the Lean Enterprise* (Jackson)
- *Measure What Matters* (Doerr)
- *The Lean Startup* (Ries)

Books on problem solving and systematic improvement

- *Managing to Learn* (Shook)
- *Understanding A3 Thinking* (Sobek)

- *The Toyota Engagement Equation* (Richardson and Richardson)
- *Gemba Kaizen* (Imai)
- *Healthcare Kaizen* (Graban and Swartz)
- *The Toyota Way to Continuous Improvement* (Liker and Franz)

A deeper dive on Process Behavior Charts and related methods

- *Making Sense of Data* (Wheeler)
- *Twenty Things You Need to Know* (Wheeler)
- *Data Sanity* (Balestracci)
- *Normality and the Process Behavior Chart* (Wheeler)

Leading change

- *Motivational Interviewing for Leadership* (Multiple Authors)

About the Author

Mark Graban is an internationally recognized consultant, published author, professional speaker, and blogger.

He builds upon a deep education in engineering and management, with practical experience working with executives and frontline employees in multiple industries to synthesize and practice methods, including Lean management, continuous improvement, statistical methods, and people-centered leadership approaches.

Mark's goal is to help others learn how to improve and sustain performance. In his healthcare work, this means improving the quality of care and patient safety, while also reducing cost and improving the workplace experience. Across multiple sectors, he focuses on improving the customer (or patient) experience, to help the development of leaders and employees, and to build stronger, more adaptive organizations for the long term.

He has learned, practiced, and taught these methodologies in settings including manufacturing, healthcare, and technology startups. Working independently since 2010, and in partnership with other consulting groups, Mark enjoys working with organizations that are looking for better ways to improve, with leaders who are willing to lead that charge.

Mark is also a Senior Advisor for healthcare clients with the firm Value Capture. He works as a Senior Advisor to the technology and software company KaiNexus.

Mark earned a Bachelor of Science in Industrial Engineering from Northwestern University as well as a Master of Science in Mechanical Engineering and an MBA as a Fellow in the MIT Sloan Leaders for Global Operations Program.

To learn more, you can visit Mark's website at www.markgraban.com.

Please Share Your Feedback and Thoughts

If you have any feedback, please email me any time at mark@markgraban.com. Feel free to schedule a phone call or web meeting with me (www.MarkGraban.com/cal) to discuss the topics in this book and your implementation efforts.

Finally, if you like the book, please tell others and write a review on Amazon.com. Anything you can do to help promote the ideas in this book would be much appreciated, whether that's sharing on social media (mainly LinkedIn) or through professional groups or societies in which you participate.

Thanks!
Mark Graban
www.MarkGraban.com
Mark@MarkGraban.com

Endnotes

1 Deming, W. Edwards, *The New Economics, 2nd Edition* (Cambridge, MA: The MIT Press, 2000), 92.

2 Wheeler, Donald J., *Making Sense of Data: SPC for the Service Sector* (Knoxville: SPC Press, 2003), 95.

3 Wheeler, Donald J, "The New Terminology," SPC Ink, 1998, no.2, Manuscript No. 129, 2.

4 Deming, W. Edwards, *Out of the Crisis, 1st MIT Press Ed.*, (Cambridge, MA: The MIT Press, 2000), 121.

5 Jackson, Thomas L., *Hoshin Kanri for the Lean Enterprise* (New York: Productivity Press, 2006), xii.

6 Ries, Eric. *The Lean Startup: How Today's Entrepreneurs Use Continuous Innovation to Create Radically Successful Businesses* (New York: Currency, 2011), 129.

7 Ries, 143.

8 Ries, Eric, *The Startup Way: How Modern Companies Use Entrepreneurial Management to Transform Culture and Drive Long-Term Growth* (New York: Random House, 2017), 103.

9 Deming, W. Edwards, *The Essential Deming: Leadership Principles from the Father of Quality* (New York: McGraw-Hill, 2012), 69.

10 Deming, W. Edwards, *Out of the Crisis, 1st MIT Press Ed.*, (Cambridge, MA: The MIT Press, 2000), 23.

11 Joiner, Brian, *Fourth Generation Management: The New Business Consciousness* (New York: McGraw-Hill, 1994), 10.

12 Graban, Mark, "Lessons from the Wells Fargo Scandal, Mismanagement, and Gaming the Numbers," https://www.leanblog.org/2016/09/some-reading-on-the-wells-fargo-scandal-and-mismanagement/.

13 Graban, Mark, "The Real #VAscandal is the Long Waiting Times & Bad Management, Not Gaming by Bad Apples," https://www.leanblog.org/2014/05/the-real-va-scandal-is-the-long-waiting-times-bad-management-not-gaming-by-bad-apples/.

14 Baer, Drake, "How Changing One Habit Helped Quintuple Alcoa's Income," http://www.businessinsider.com/how-changing-one-habit-quintupled-alcoas-income-2014-4.

15 Dennis, Pascal, *Lean Production Simplified, Third Edition* (Productivity Press: New York, 2015), 30.

16 Ries, Eric, *The Lean Startup: How Today's Entrepreneurs Use Continuous Innovation to Create Radically Successful Businesses* (Currency: New York, 2011), 280.

17 Ries, Eric. *The Lean Startup: How Today's Entrepreneurs Use Continuous Innovation to Create Radically Successful Businesses* (New York: Currency, 2011), 128.

18 Wheeler, Donald J., *Understanding Variation: The Key to Managing Chaos, Second Edition* (Knoxville: SPC Press, 2000), 13.

19 NHS Improvement, "Making Data Count," https://improvement.nhs.uk/documents/2748/NHS_MAKING_DATA_COUNT_FINAL.pdf.

20 Deming, W. Edwards, *The New Economics, 2nd Edition* (Cambridge, MA: The MIT Press, 2000), 98.

21 Wheeler, Donald J., *Understanding Variation: The Key to Managing Chaos, Second Edition* (Knoxville: SPC Press, 2000), 4.

22 Wheeler, Donald J., *Making Sense of Data: SPC for the Service Sector* (Knoxville: SPC Press, 2003), 97.

23 Wheeler, Donald J., *Understanding Variation: The Key to Managing Chaos, Second Edition* (Knoxville: SPC Press, 2000), 30.

24 Deming, W. Edwards, *The Essential Deming: Leadership Principles from the Father of Quality* (New York: McGraw-Hill, 2012), 170.

25 Ries, Eric. *The Lean Startup: How Today's Entrepreneurs Use Continuous Innovation to Create Radically Successful Businesses* (New York: Currency, 2011), 284.

26 Toyota Motor Corporation, "Ask 'why' five times about every matter," March 2006, http://www.

toyota-global.com/company/toyota_traditions/quality/mar_apr_2006.html.

27   Graban, Mark, *Lean Hospitals: Improving Quality, Patient Safety, and Employee Engagement* (New York: Productivity Press, 2016), 160.

28   Ries, Eric, *The Lean Startup: How Today's Entrepreneurs Use Continuous Innovation to Create Radically Successful Businesses* (New York: Currency, 2011), 231.

29   Toyota Motor Corporation.

30   Goldsmith, Robert H., *Toyota's 8-Steps to Problem Solving* (NP, 2014), 9.

31   Richardson, Tracey and Ernie, *The Toyota Engagement Equation: How to Understand and Implement Continuous Improvement Thinking in Any Organization* (New York: McGraw-Hill, 2017), 87.

32   Wolterman, Dan and Dr. M. Michael Shabot, "A new standard," *Modern Healthcare*, August 1, 2011. http://www.modernhealthcare.com/article/20110801/MAGAZINE/308019973.

33   Lohr, Steve, "He Taught the Japanese," *The New York Times*, May 10, 1981, https://www.nytimes.com/1981/05/10/business/he-taught-the-japanese.html.

34   Boysen, Philip G. "Just Culture: A Foundation for Balanced Accountability and Patient Safety." The *Ochsner Journal* 13.3 (2013): 400–406. Print.

35   *BBC News Magazine*, "Can chance make you a killer?," http://www.bbc.co.uk/news/magazine-10729380.

36   *NBC News*, "American Airlines apologizes for flight delays, cancellations," September 21, 2012, http://overheadbin.nbcnews.com/_news/2012/09/21/14017618-american-airlines-apologizes-for-flight-delays-cancellations.

37   Flint, Joe, "Academy Awards Pull In Record-Low Ratings," March 5, 2018, https://www.wsj.com/articles/academy-awards-pull-in-record-low-ratings-1520285405.

38   McClintock, Pamela, "Oscars 2012: Is There a Recipe for Ratings Success?," *The Hollywood Reporter*, February 13, 2012.

39   Smith, James M. *Meaningful Graphs: Converting Data into Informative Excel Charts.* (n.p.: James M. Smith, 2014), 16.

40   Smith, 3.

41   Graban, Mark and Joseph E. Swartz, *Healthcare Kaizen: Engaging Front-Line Staff in Sustainable Continuous Improvements* (New York: Productivity Press, 2012), 4.

42   Wilcox, Jason; Kersh, Brian; Jenkins, Elizabeth. *Motivational Interviewing for Leadership: MI-LEAD*, (Gray Beach Publishing: Roseburg, OR), 2017), 16.

43   Prosci, "ADKAR," https://www.prosci.com/adkar.

44   Prosci, What is the ADKAR Model, https://www.prosci.com/adkar/adkar-model.

45   Kotter, Inc, "8-Step Process," https://www.kotterinc.com/8-steps-process-for-leading-change/

46   ExperiencePoint, "Change Theory," unpublished paper, 2016.

47   Wheeler, Donald J., "Myths About Process Behavior Charts," https://www.qualitydigest.com/inside/quality-insider-article/myths-about-process-behavior-charts.html.

48   Wheeler, Donald J., *Making Sense of Data: SPC for the Service Sector* (Knoxville: SPC Press, 2003), 97.

49   *Ibid*, 165.

50   Wheeler, Donald J. and Rip Stauffer, "When Should We Use Extra Detection Rules?," Quality Digest, https://www.qualitydigest.com/inside/statistics-column/when-should-we-use-extra-detection-rules-100917.html.

TARGET vs GOALS → Long Term

↳ Short Term   Ideal Objective

Helps keep focus
+ gauge progress
towards our GOAL

Percentile Rank, LOS

Made in the USA
Monee, IL
01 November 2019